Understanding Electronic Control of Energy Systems

Written by: Don L. Cannon, Ph.D
Assoc. Prof. of Electrical Engineering
University of Texas at Arlington
Staff Consultant, Texas Instruments Learning Center

With contributions by: Gerald Luecke, MSEE
Mgr. Technical Products Development
Texas Instruments Learning Center

Editor: Charles W. Battle
Texas Instruments Learning Center Staff

TEXAS INSTRUMENTS
INCORPORATED
P.O. BOX 225012, MS-54 ● DALLAS, TEXAS 75265

This book was developed by:
The Staff of the Texas Instruments Learning Center
P.O. Box 225012 MS-54
Dallas, Texas 75265

For marketing and distribution inquire to:
James B. Allen
Marketing Manager
P.O. Box 225012, MS-54
Dallas, Texas 75265

Appreciation is expressed to:
Gerald L. Ward and H. Steven Myers of Dallas Power and Light Company and
Frank Shants of Texas Utilities Services, Inc. for their source information
and comments.
E. L. Johnson, Dan Mosher, Kirby Nelson, Howard McCalla, Bill Culwell,
Cecil Presnell, Jack Mahaffey and Cam Wason for their source information
and/or comments.
Allan Shaffer, Hank Nystrom, Don Falk, Rob Kleinstueber and Nancy
Plunkett for their help.

Word Processing:
Judy Justis
Pamela Starnes

Artwork and layout by:
Plunk & Associates

ISBN 0-89512-051-8
Library of Congress Catalog Number: 81-85602

Table of Contents

Preface

This book is about energy—its sources, its types, its forms. It is for the person who has an interest in how electronics can be used to control energy in its many forms and how electronic systems help to use energy efficiently, safely, effectively and for increased productivity. In today's world, we are all striving to conserve energy. As energy costs soar and energy supplies dwindle, it becomes increasingly critical for us to understand how we can more effectively utilize the energy supplies we have. The key to efficient and productive use of energy is to provide precise control over its use by individuals and corporations. Such precise control is available through the use of modern electronic and computer control systems.

Understanding the electronic control of energy begins with understanding the primary and secondary sources of energy; the mechanical, electrical, thermal, chemical and light (solar) forms of energy and the conversions between them. Then, fundamental control functions are reviewed to understand how electronics can be used to implement these functions. Next, the "how to control" chapters of the book concentrate on those systems which consume the largest portion of our energy supplies and a large portion of our earnings each year. These systems include electrical motors, lighting, heating and air conditioning, and automotive systems.

Throughout the discussion of these energy systems, explanations of the control techniques that have been used are given. More importantly, the control techniques of the present and future using programmable energy control systems are explained. These programmable control systems may be special purpose systems, or ones using general purpose computers. In either case, the task that the standard hardware performs can be changed as the application changes by just reprogramming the system. The last chapter of the book deals specifically with how such computer-based control systems can manage the use of energy in a large industrial plant and save significant energy dollars by providing better energy utilization.

Like other books in the series, this book builds understanding step-by-step. Try to master each chapter before going on to the next one. Some readers experienced in electronics may elect to bypass Chapter 3; however, it does serve as a good review. A quiz is provided at the end of each chapter for self-evaluation of what has been learned. Answers are given at the back of the book.

The need for energy is projected to grow and grow in the future. Our success as a nation may depend on how well we use the energy that we have. We hope this book brings a sense of understanding of how electronics can help to use energy more productively.

D.C.
G.L.

Major Sources of Energy

ABOUT THIS BOOK

The progress of people in the areas of productivity, technology, and standard of living has been paced by their ability to discover and utilize energy resources. The very security and well-being of people depend on the availability of energy. Their economic and technological success depends ultimately on how efficiently they use their available energy resources. Their standard and quality of life depends on how well they can control the use of energy and how successful they are in discovering new energy sources. This is where electronics comes in.

Electronic devices provide the most sophisticated techniques of controlling our environment and our machines. The most advanced methods of detecting patterns which may lead to the discovery of energy resources is through the proper use of electronic computers. Since energy will continue to be of vital importance to us through the coming century and beyond, it is of equal importance that we understand how electronics can contribute to the efficient use of energy. The purpose of this book is to help provide this understanding, beginning with a view of what energy is and how we have used it in the past.

WHAT IS ENERGY?

Energy touches all of us during each day of our lives. It has received extensive coverage in the news media over the last decade. As a result, most of us have a greater understanding of what energy is and realize how important it is. Most of us understand what it means to be energetic, and the difference between the energy required for hard work versus that required for easy work. We know the names and principal characteristics of most of the common forms of energy. This common knowledge may be inaccurate in some ways, but it does provide a good starting point for examining the concepts of energy and work.

Relation of Energy, Work, Force and Power

Energy

The concepts of energy and work are closely related since one classical definition for energy is in terms of the concept of work:

Energy is the Capacity for Doing Work.

Of course, for this definition to mean anything, there must be a corresponding definition for work.

Work and Force

Elementary physics textbooks define work as:

Work is Performed When a Material Mass is Moved
From One Position to Another.

In order to accomplish such movement of a material mass, sufficient force must be applied to the mass to move the mass. (A common misconception is that mass and weight are the same thing; however, mass and weight are equal only at sea level on earth. Weight is related to gravitational force and changes with altitude; mass does not change.) By this definition of work, no work is accomplished if no movement takes place even if force is applied. For example, if you push as hard as you can against a brick wall and don't move the wall, then no work has been done even though you have applied force.

As mentioned previously, some types of work require a great deal of energy and other types of work require little energy. Moving large rocks or pushing a car requires considerable energy while writing with a pencil or pushing a toy car requires relatively little energy. In all these efforts, a force is required to move an object. To move a small object over a short distance, very little force or effort is required and very little energy is used. However, if that small object is moved over a long distance, more energy is used because more work is done. The amount of work done can be calculated by the equation:

$$Work = Force \times Distance$$

Said in words,

Work Equals Force Times the Distance a Mass is Moved

This is illustrated in *Figure 1-1*. A person is pictured pushing a cart. If the cart requires a force of 20 pounds to move it, and the person pushes it for 100 feet, the person does 2,000 foot-pounds of work. If the person pushes the cart for another 100 feet the person does another 2,000 foot-pounds of work. This is a total of 4,000 foot-pounds of work for a distance of 200 feet. Notice that this is the work required to move the cart only and does not consider the work required to move the person.

Power

Another term related to energy and work is power. The dimension of time is considered for power; that is, how much work is done in a given amount of time:

Power is the Rate of Doing Work

Power is calculated by dividing work by time. Twice the amount of power is required to do the same amount of work in one-half the time.

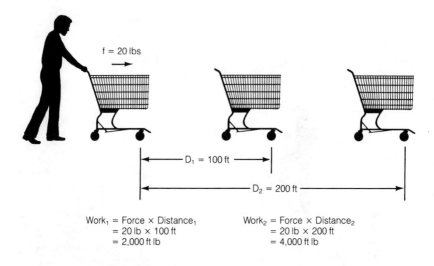

$$Work_1 = Force \times Distance_1 \qquad Work_2 = Force \times Distance_2$$
$$= 20\ lb \times 100\ ft \qquad\qquad = 20\ lb \times 200\ ft$$
$$= 2{,}000\ ft\ lb \qquad\qquad\quad = 4{,}000\ ft\ lb$$

Figure 1-1. *Relation of Force, Distance, and Work*

Figure 1-2 illustrates this relation. In this example, a person weighing 100 pounds climbs a flight of stairs one step at a time. The vertical distance from the lower floor to the upper floor is 10 feet. It takes 50 seconds to climb the stairs. On another occasion, this same person is in a hurry, so he/she runs up the stairs, taking two at a time. It takes only 25 seconds this time. As calculated in *Figure 1-2*, the same amount of work, 1,000 foot-pounds, is done each time the person climbs the stairs. However, when the work is done in one-half the time, twice as much power is required. (Note that when work in the vertical direction is calculated, the amount of movement in the horizontal direction is ignored.)

Doing work such as lifting heavy rocks, digging ditches, or pushing cars requires a large amount of force or exertion. If we are rested and fresh, we have more energy than if we are tired. The more energy we have, the more work we are capable of performing.

It is the same with non-human sources of energy. The more energy available, the larger the mass that can be moved, or the greater the distance it can be moved, or the faster it can be moved, assuming that enough force can be generated to move the mass.

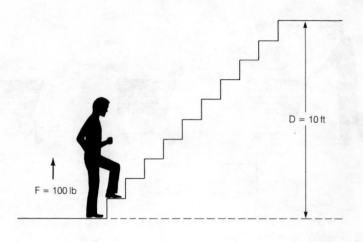

Work = Force × Distance
    = 100 lb × 10 ft
    = 1,000 ft lbs

Time_1 = 50 seconds
Time_2 = 25 seconds

Power = Work/Time

P_{t1} = 1,000 ft lb/50 sec
    = 20 ft lb/sec

P_{t2} = 1,000 ft lb/25 sec
    = 40 ft lb/sec

1 Horsepower = 550 ft lb/sec

HP_{t1} = 20/550
    = 0.036 Hp

HP_{t2} = 40/550
    = 0.073 Hp

Figure 1-2. *Relation of Work and Power*

Kinetic and Potential Energy

Any definition of energy must consider the forms of energy. This is not the same idea as the sources of energy, but is related to the general forms that energy takes. One of these forms is kinetic energy. Kinetic energy is the energy involved with a *mass in motion* at a certain speed or velocity. The other form is potential energy. Potential energy is the energy associated with the *relative position* of a material mass. Energy is found in both forms and energy is usually always being changed from potential to kinetic and back. An example shown in *Figure 1-3* that is familiar to most of us is riding a bicycle.

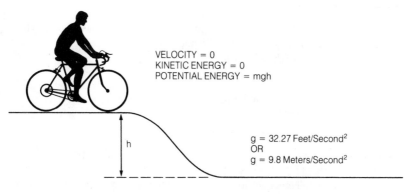

a. Bicycle with Potential Energy but no Kinetic Energy

b. Potential Energy Converted into Kinetic Energy

Figure 1-3. *Kinetic and Potential Energy*

In this example, the bicycle positioned at the top of the hill in *Figure 1-3a* has a certain amount of potential energy relative to the position of the bottom of the hill because the force of gravity is trying to pull it (as well as everything else) to the center of the earth. It has no kinetic energy because it is not moving. If we start the bicycle from a standstill at the top of the hill with a slight push, the bicycle will coast down the hill, picking up speed as it goes. By the time the bicycle reaches the bottom of the hill, as shown in *Figure 1-3b*, the potential energy is converted to kinetic energy. As the bicycle coasts along the level stretch, the kinetic energy is converted to heat by the friction of the tires on the pavement and the resistance of the air, and the bicycle gradually slows to a stop.

The reverse of this situation occurs when a bicycle approaches the hill from the bottom at a speed sufficient to coast up the hill and reach the top of the hill. In this case, the kinetic energy built up by pedaling on the flat road is converted to potential energy as the bicycle coasts up the hill. At the top of the hill, it has reached the maximum potential energy possible for that location.

We can say the potential energy is stored as a result of the bicycle being at the top of the hill; that is, in its position in space. We can say that the kinetic energy is the energy stored in the mass moving at a velocity. The equation for kinetic energy is:

$$\text{Kinetic Energy} = m\, v^2/2$$

where m is the mass of the moving body and v is its speed or velocity. The equation for gravitational potential energy is:

$$\text{Potential Energy} = m\, g\, h$$

where m again is the mass of the body, g is the constant related to the gravitational force [32.2 ft/second^2 (9.8 meters/second^2)] and h is the height of the body above some reference level. There are many other types of potential energy and these will be discussed throughout the book.

Conservation of Energy

Another fact about energy that is very important in its use and control is that energy can be converted from one form to another, but is not destroyed. In fact, the classical law of energy conservation is:

Energy can be Converted from One Form to Another,
But it Cannot be Destroyed.

In the bicycle example, the potential energy at the top of the hill was converted to kinetic energy. Then the kinetic energy was converted to heat. This heat, along with many other sources of heat, is stored in the earth's atmosphere as potential energy and contributes to weather cycles. For the uphill portion of the example, the potential energy of food is converted by the body to kinetic energy of the muscles which is transferred to the bicycle by the rider. As the bicycle goes up the hill, the kinetic energy is converted to potential energy.

The classical law was expressed and verified by early physicists, but with the discovery of atomic energy, physicists determined that the law had to be modified slightly when nuclear effects were taken into account. The modern version of the law of conservation of energy is:

The Total Mass and Energy in the Universe is
Constant Though They can be Converted from
One Form to Another.

This allows for the conversion of mass into energy that occurs in certain nuclear reactions. It still includes the feature of the law that allows the conversion of energy from one form to another such as potential into kinetic or mechanical into electrical and so on. The techniques of these conversions will be examined in more detail in the next chapter.

WHAT ARE THE MAJOR SOURCES OF ENERGY?

The sources of energy can be categorized as primary sources and secondary sources. These sources are related as shown in *Figure 1-4*.

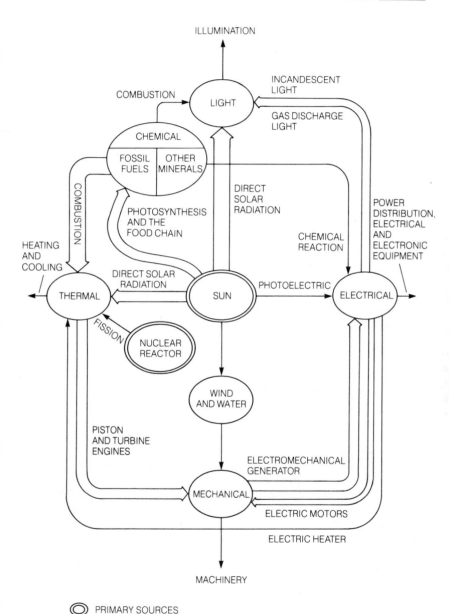

Figure 1-4. *The Energy Conversion Chain*

Primary Sources

All energy comes from two primary sources. These are shown as the sun and the man-made nuclear reactor. Since the sun is a huge nuclear reactor, then nuclear energy is the primary source of all our energy. Still, it is more convenient to separate the sun from the man-made reactor. The man-made reactor generates energy directly from atoms of raw material from the earth and is independent of all other energy sources; therefore, it is considered as a primary source.

Secondary Sources

All other sources available to us may be traced directly to the sun. The best examples of this are the fossil fuels (coal, oil, and gas) which were formed from vegetation produced by the sun thousands of years ago. Therefore, all energy sources other than the sun and the nuclear reactor are considered as secondary sources.

Direct Sources

Energy sources may also be classified as direct or indirect. A direct source is one whose energy is useful just as it is without modification or conversion. The sun definitely fits this category because its radiation directly warms the earth and provides light for the earth. The kinetic energy of the wind can be used directly to push a sailing ship or support a glider.

Indirect Sources

An indirect source is one whose energy form must be changed to be useful. All sources other than the sun and wind are indirect. In fact, the sun and wind also can be included in the indirect classification, since solar and wind energy can be converted into other useful forms. Solar energy can be converted to electrical energy. Energy from the wind can turn windmills to provide mechanical energy directly or the mechanical energy can be converted to electrical energy.

The kinetic energy of running or falling water is an important secondary source of energy. The naturally running water of rivers and streams can turn water wheels to produce mechanical energy. More often, the falling water is artificially produced by collecting large amounts of water behind a dam. The water in the reservoir is then released as desired to drive water turbines for mechanical energy. The mechanical energy is usually used to produce electrical energy.

Probably the most important secondary source of energy is the chemical energy stored in wood and the fossil fuels of coal, oil, gas and the fuels obtained from them. This energy is essentially stored solar energy from the photosynthesis of sunlight by plants. This source is classified as indirect since the chemical energy must be converted to another form. Most often, it is converted to heat or thermal energy by combustion (burning) of the fuel. Some light energy also is produced by the combustion. This light could be the primary reason for the burning, but may be only a by-product of the burning.

Another type of chemical energy is that produced by chemical reactions between certain raw materials or processed materials from the earth. Explosives such as dynamite and nitroglycerin are results of such chemical reaction and these are certainly useful forms of energy. A more common form is the electrical energy produced by the chemical reactions in a battery.

The useful energy from a nuclear reactor is thermal energy. It is the conversion product of the nuclear reactions of the atoms of certain materials obtained from the earth.

The thermal energy from nuclear reactors and from the combustion of fossil fuels may be used directly as a source of heat or the thermal energy may be converted to mechanical energy, mainly by various types of engines. Electrical energy may be converted to thermal energy for a source of heat.

The mechanical energy produced from the various conversions may be used to power machines or to drive electrical generators.

Electrical energy may be used directly to power various types of electrical or electronic equipment or it may be distributed to be converted to other forms. It may be converted to light energy, mechanical energy, or thermal energy. Electrical energy is the most versatile form and the easiest to use form of energy.

HOW IS ENERGY STORED AND TRANSPORTED?

The techniques of energy storage depend on the type of energy. The energy storage inherent in the potential energy of the chemical bonds of wood, gas, coal, and oil are examples of natural storage. These energy sources may be transported from the discovery location to the point where they are used fairly easily, particularly in the case of oil and gas.

The potential energy associated with water in an elevated reservoir is stored energy, but in a form that is not transportable. Thus, this type of energy must be converted to electrical form and the electrical energy transmitted to the point where it will be used.

Certain types of energy cannot be stored in the present form, but must be converted to another form for storage. Wind and solar energy are often converted to electrical energy. If the electrical energy is not used immediately it is often stored in batteries in the form of chemical energy. Also, solar energy is often stored as thermal energy in large heat sinks made of rocks or other heat absorbing materials.

Mechanical energy in most cases is difficult to store and may present problems in transmitting it over more than moderate distances. A spring, such as that used in a mechanical clock, is a means of storing mechanical energy. The cable cars of San Francisco and the drilling of oil wells into the earth are two examples of systems that transport mechanical energy over long distances, one by a cable and the other by coupling steel pipe together. But because of the transportation difficulties, the mechanical energy is usually generated where it's used.

Thus, of all the secondary energy sources illustrated in *Figure 1-4*, only chemical energy offers both efficient storage and simple transportation of energy. None of the others combine both of these features, even though electrical energy can be easily transported and can be directly converted to any of the other useful forms of energy at the use location.

The primary energy source of nuclear energy has energy storage similar to chemical energy. The energy is stored in the nucleus of atoms in certain materials which can be transported easily to the nuclear reactor. The reactor, in turn, converts this atomic energy to some form that is usable and can be easily transported, usually electrical. At the present time, it is not possible to convert the nuclear energy directly at the point where it's used except to power very large transports such as ships or submarines. This is because nuclear energy conversion requires a large and expensive plant which cannot be placed in just any location. It certainly is not practical at this time to power a car or heat and cool an individual building from a self-contained nuclear conversion plant.

HOW IS ENERGY USED?

Historically, the first use of energy by people was simply the natural heating provided by the solar energy from the sun and the chemical energy of food converted to muscle power. The discovery of fire provided the use of the chemical energy stored in wood and other materials for heat and light. It also provided the capability of cooking food for the first time.

The domestication of animals permitted the use of the stronger muscles of animals to provide the energy for farming and other commercial activities. Wind energy was used to drive the sails of ships for improved commerce and exploration. Later in history, the energy in flowing water was tapped through the use of water mills.

This early energy usage of solar, wind and water continued until the development of steam engines and pumps in the 1700's. These engines converted the chemical energy of wood and coal to mechanical energy, and greatly expanded the amount of mechanical power available to perform the heavy work of the early days of the industrial revolution. With these engines, steamships replaced sailing ships, steam locomotives became available for transporting large loads of goods and people over long distances, and engines capable of performing heavy manufacturing operations became available. It was the development of the steam engine that made the move to modern industry possible. The development of the internal combustion engine using kerosene or gasoline in the middle 1800's provided even more power for modern industry and provided the basis for building the elaborate transportation system we have today.

As electricity was understood, it became possible to generate and control electrical energy and develop electric motors. This opened the way to modern energy utilization and modern day electronic technology. The most recent historical developments in the use of energy were the discovery of how nuclear particles react to release energy and the harnessing of that energy for practical use in nuclear power plants to generate electricity or to propel ships.

Major Portions of Energy Use

Figure 1-4 summarizes the current state of the use of the available energy sources and how they are being applied in modern society to serve our needs. The first major portion of the resources are used to provide year-round comfort for humans through the use of heating and air conditioning systems which can meet the requirements of almost any location.

A second major use is to provide individual and commercial transportation to travel great distances in a short time for business and pleasure. Without the resulting complex transportation network, the goods needed for worldwide commerce, exploration, education and pleasure would not be available.

The third major portion of energy is used for agriculture, mining, and manufacturing to supply the goods that serve our basic needs and provide the things that make life easier and more pleasurable. These goods in themselves are consumers of energy.

The fourth major portion of energy is used for lighting homes, streets, office buildings, manufacturing plants, and shopping centers. Working conditions are improved, while time for work and time for play are extended by modern lighting. Electric lighting has contributed greatly to the advancement of society.

The fifth major portion of energy is used for the complex, world-wide communications network that includes radio, television, telephone, and computer networks. Imagine what life would be without the daily news broadcasts, the world-wide coverage of the Olympics, the United Nations meetings, the presidential elections, the soap operas, the daily newspaper, and the capability to talk to grandmother a thousand miles away at any time. Each day the world seems to get smaller because of the expansion of the extensive communications capability.

WHAT HAVE WE LEARNED?

1. Energy is the capability to perform work.
2. Work is the movement of a material object (a mass) through a distance by applying a force to the object.
3. Power is the rate of doing work.
4. Energy takes one of two general forms: kinetic or potential energy.
5. Mass can be converted into energy and energy can be converted from one form to another.
6. The primary sources of all energy are the sun and nuclear energy.
7. The main secondary sources of energy are wind, elevated water reservoirs, and chemical reactions.
8. The most commonly used forms of energy are electrical, thermal, mechanical, and light energy.

Quiz for Chapter 1

1. A primary source of energy on earth is:
   a. work
   b. the sun
   c. water
   d. wind

2. Man's first use of energy was in the form of:
   a. electrical energy
   b. mechanical energy
   c. chemical energy
   d. solar energy

3. The first form of non-human energy used for transportation by sea was:
   a. steam engines
   b. wind energy
   c. nuclear reactors
   d. electrical motors

4. A form of energy that provides for convenient storage of energy is:
   a. chemical
   b. electrical
   c. mechanical
   d. thermal

5. Electrical energy is very useful because:
   a. it is easily transported
   b. it can be converted to other forms easily
   c. it can be generated from other forms easily
   d. all of the above

6. The forms of energy that are useful to man include:
   a. chemical
   b. electrical
   c. mechanical
   d. thermal
   e. light
   f. nuclear
   g. all of the above

7. If an object is raised from 10 to 20 feet above a reference level, how much has its potential energy changed?
   a. halved
   b. doubled
   c. quadrupled
   d. no change

8. An elevator exerts a force on the cables of 1,100 pounds. How fast (in seconds) can 1 horsepower raise the elevator 10 feet?
   a. 5
   b. 10
   c. 20
   d. 40

9. Most fossil fuel energy is used to produce:
   a. heat
   b. light
   c. electricity through direct conversion

10. Lighting is provided primarily from energy in the form of:
   a. chemical
   b. electrical
   c. mechanical

11. The primary output of nuclear reactor energy is in the form of:
   a. electrical
   b. mechanical
   c. light
   d. thermal

12. Most nuclear reactors are the following type:
   a. fission
   b. fusion

Energy Conversion

ABOUT THIS CHAPTER

Of all of the available energy on earth, the warming radiation and light of the sun (solar energy) and the resulting wind and water power are of direct use to man. All other forms of available energy must be converted from an existing form into the form of energy needed in a given situation. This chapter discusses the most used techniques presently available for converting energy from one form into another needed form.

WHAT ARE THE USEFUL FORMS OF ENERGY?

Since all of us are energy consumers, we have a good idea of the commonly used forms of energy. They are thermal (heat or cool), light, mechanical, and electrical energy. *Figure 2-1* (a repeat of *Figure 1-4*) summarizes these useful forms of energy as they are related to primary sources and to each other. In this figure, the conversions from one form to another are shown as arrows, with the width of the arrow indicating the relative amounts of energy involved. Much of the energy used is for the production of thermal energy to provide heating and cooling with a majority of it used for heating (raising the temperature of a material and its surroundings).

HOW IS THERMAL ENERGY GENERATED?

Aside from the readily available heat from the sun, there are three major techniques for generating thermal energy for the purpose of heating: electrical, chemical, and nuclear.

Electrical

The conversion of electrical energy into heat is accomplished by forcing an electric current through a resistance. The resistive heating elements may be directly exposed to produce radiant heat as is done in the small space heaters that some people use in their homes. Electric toasters and electric ovens also are included in applications of this type. To heat large areas, the resistive heating elements are placed directly in a moving air flow and the heated air is circulated through the area by a blower. This arrangement is called an electric furnace. The electric furnace itself is relatively efficient since almost all of the electrical energy is converted to heat; however, the overall efficiency when the electric power generation from fossil fuels is included is usually lower than if the heat is produced directly by the burning (combustion) of the fossil fuel in a furnace right at the place the heat is being used.

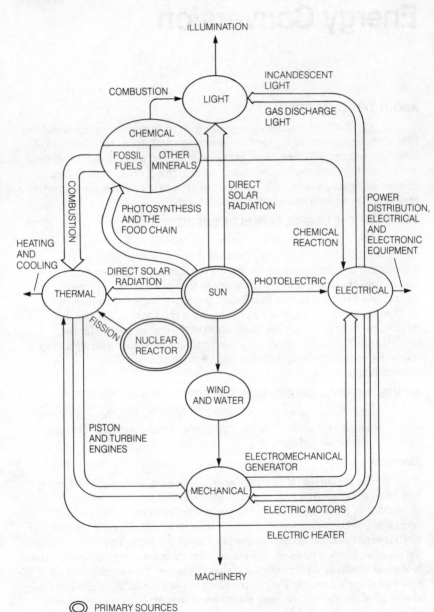

Figure 2-1. The Energy Conversion Chain

Chemical

The direct generation of heat from the combustion of fossil fuel chemical energy sources such as wood, coal, oil or gas is the major method used to produce heat for residential and business use. It is a very efficient method for heating areas or materials, with over 50 percent of the energy available in the fuel being converted to useful thermal energy. The heat may be used directly to heat a material or an area, but often the heat is transferred to a moving air flow through a heat exchanger so that the heat can be distributed easily to wherever it is needed.

Nuclear

The third major source of thermal energy is nuclear energy produced on earth. Of course, the radiation produced by nuclear fusion on the sun warms the environment and reduces the amount of heat that must be generated by other means. The nuclear fission reaction produced in man-made nuclear reactors releases large amounts of thermal energy; however, this thermal energy is not useful directly in heating applications for residential or commercial use. Generally, the thermal energy is used to produce mechanical energy which can be used directly (e.g. to power a ship) or converted to electrical form for later conversion into thermal energy at the place where it is used (e.g. to heat a building or run a machine).

The principle behind all nuclear energy conversion is the energy and mass relationship developed by Einstein which states that mass can be converted into energy:

$$\text{Energy} = mc^2$$

where m = mass and c is the velocity (Speed = distance per second) of light. If the metric system is used, m is in kilograms (1 Kg = 2.2 lbs at sea level) and c is in meters per second (1 meter = 3.28 ft), and c^2 in Einstein's equation equals 9×10^{16} meters^2/second^2. The resulting energy is in joules; thus, each kilogram of mass can be converted into 9 x 10^{16} joules of energy. Normally, an electric company sends a bill for the number of kilowatt-hours (KWH) used. One joule = 2.778×10^{-7} KWH, so 9×10^{16} joules = 2.5×10^{10} KWH of electrical energy. One joule = 9.481×10^{-4} BTU, so 9×10^{16} joules = 8.53×10^{13} BTUs of thermal energy. About 3 billion kilograms of coal would have to be burned to get the same number of BTU's. This is why nuclear energy is so promising; that is, a very small amount of nuclear fuel can provide the same energy as enormous amounts of fossil fuels.

Fusion

There are two types of nuclear reactions that can be used to produce energy: fusion and fission. Fusion is theoretically much more powerful and efficient than fission. Fusion involves the joining of atoms in the presence of extremely high temperature. Unfortunately, the only fusion technology currently available to mankind is the hydrogen bomb. Controlled fusion reactions are not yet possible; therefore, fusion power plants are still a technology of the future.

Fission

Fission nuclear power plants have become rather commonplace and they all use some variation of the reactions shown in *Figure 2-2*. In the non-breeder reactor, a neutron bombards a uranium atom and causes the uranium atom to split into two other atoms. In the example shown in *Figure 2-2*, the reaction produces intermediate products of xenon and strontium. These are unstable and decay into the stable atoms of lanthanum and molybdenum, and produce two neutrons and 7 electrons. If the computed mass of the original atom and neutron is compared to the computed mass of the final products, it is found that mass has been lost. This mass has been converted to the kinetic energy of the atoms, electrons, and neutrons produced by the reaction. This kinetic energy can be converted to usable heat in a suitable absorbing material.

Notice that the single neutron that triggered the initial reaction of converting a stable uranium atom (shown in *Figure 2-2* as $_{92}U^{235}$) into an unstable atom ($_{92}U^{236}$) has produced two neutrons of relatively high kinetic energy. If these two neutrons impact two more uranium atoms, four such neutrons will be produced. This avalanching effect rapidly accumulates to involve most of the atoms of the material, with the mass loss for each reaction mounting to huge equivalents of energy. This avalanching effect is allowed in the fission atomic bomb with the resulting devastation caused by the tremendous release of energy.

Obviously, the avalanching cannot be allowed in a nuclear reactor designed to convert the energy of the atom into usable forms of energy. To control the energy release, the reactor design must ensure that, on the average, one of the two product neutrons are captured by an absorbing material and the other neutron is allowed to impact other uranium atoms. In this way, the reaction can be sustained with a continual release of energy in a controlled manner. The rate of production of neutrons is controlled by the position of absorbing material rods in the uranium core of the reactor.

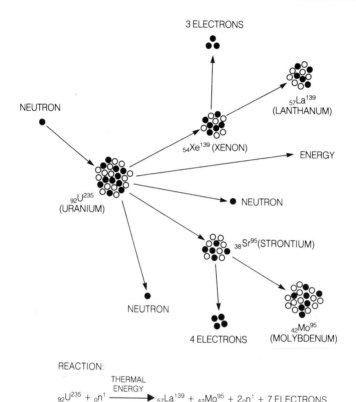

REACTION:

$$_{92}U^{235} + {}_0n^1 \xrightarrow{\text{THERMAL ENERGY}} {}_{57}La^{139} + {}_{42}Mo^{95} + 2{}_0n^1 + 7 \text{ ELECTRONS}$$

Figure 2-2. *Nuclear Fission*
(Source: E. M. Walsh, Energy Conversion, *Ronald Press, 1967)*

To capture the useful energy, the high kinetic energy of the atoms, electrons and neutrons is converted to heat by absorbing the kinetic energy with a shell of material surrounding the reactor. This thermal energy can be used directly, converted to mechanical energy, or converted to electrical energy. The overall conversion process illustrated in *Figure 2-2* is very simplified. A much more extensive discussion covering the details of the reactions as well as the alternative reactions available and considerations of the control of such nuclear power generation will be covered in a later chapter.

As shown in *Figure 2-1*, thermal energy also is a link in the conversion chain from chemical to mechanical. This will be covered in the section on mechanical energy.

HOW IS LIGHT ENERGY GENERATED?

The primary source of daytime lighting is direct radiation from the sun. Generation of light by humans for general area lighting is accomplished by two methods: incandescent and gas discharge. Light also can be produced by certain semiconductor devices and by direct radiation, but this light is of low power and is not suitable for general illumination.

Basic Process

The principle mechanism used to generate light is that of increasing the energy level of electrons in the atoms of appropriate chemical elements or compounds. Electrons in orbit in the atom can exist at a number of energy levels, but they tend to change toward their lowest energy configuration. Thus, after electrons are given added energy by energy external to the atom, they fall back to their lower energy state and lose the added energy by releasing it in the form of light radiation. The basic process is illustrated in *Figure 2-3*.

In *Figure 2-3a*, the idealized view of a one electron atom (hydrogen) is illustrated in its low energy state; that is, the electron is in the orbit nearest to the nucleus. When the atom is exposed to an external energy source such as light radiation, thermal energy, or electrical energy, the electron can be given enough energy to move to a higher energy orbit (an orbit further away from the nucleus) as shown in *Figure 2-3b*. Eventually, this electron will fall back to its normal lower orbit (*Figure 2-3c*), releasing the change in energy as light radiation of a certain frequency or "color".

If this light radiation is in the range of frequencies that is detectable by the human eye, it is called visible light. If the frequency is lower than this visible range (closer spaced orbits), it is called infrared radiation. This is the type of radiation from heat lamps. If the light has a frequency higher than that of visible light (wide orbit spacing), the light energy is in the ultraviolet or X-ray range, both of which are useful in modern society.

Thus, to generate light radiation, all that is required is to provide enough energy to an appropriate chemical material to cause its electrons to move to the higher energy level orbits of the atoms of the material. When these electrons fall back into their normal orbits near the nucleus of the atom, light is generated.

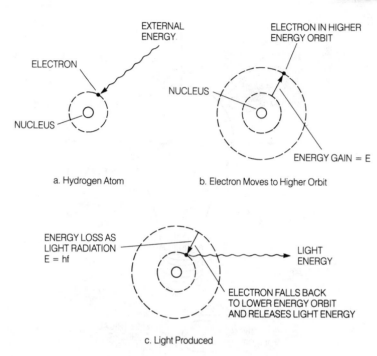

Figure 2-3. Generation of Light

Incandescent Light

Incandescent light is produced when electrons are excited by thermal energy. Thus, the glow of hot coals or hot metal is incandescent light. Electrical energy can be converted to incandescent light energy through the use of the incandescent lamp, commonly called a light bulb, as shown in *Figure 2-4*.

Incandescent Lamp

In this lamp, an electrical current flows through a resistive element called a filament. It is contained in a sealed bulb that has been evacuated; i.e., all the air has been pumped out. When an electrical current is forced to flow through the tungsten filament, the filament gets hot. The heat provides external energy to raise the energy level of the electrons in the filament material so they move to higher orbits. When they return to their normal orbits, the released energy produces visible light. The electrons are excited again to the higher level, then fall back again to the lower level. This continual process of energy level change provides a continual flow of light energy. Unfortunately, most of the electrical energy used by the incandescent lamp is wasted in the form of heat with only about 5 percent converted to light energy.

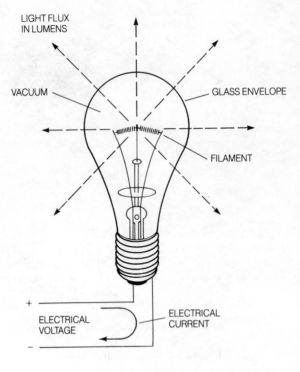

a. Incandescent Lamp

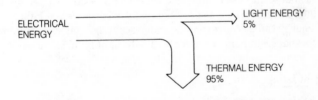

b. Conversion Efficiency

Figure 2-4. Conversion of Electrical Energy to Light Energy Using Incandescent Lamp

Gas Discharge Light

Light generation using the gas discharge method is somewhat more direct. Electric current which flows ionizes the gas and excites the electrons of gas atoms directly rather than producing heat which excites the electrons. The most commonly used type of gas discharge lamp is the fluorescent lamp.

Fluorescent Lamp

The operation of the fluorescent lamp is illustrated in *Figure 2-5*. The tube is filled with a gas which is ionized by an electric arc when the lamp is first turned on. Once started, an electric current is carried by the ionized gas atoms. These are atoms which have their outer electrons removed. Electrons from the current flow continue to collide with gas molecules to keep the gas in an ionized state. At the same time, individual gas atoms are increasing and decreasing in energy level. As the electrons fall to lower orbits, ultraviolet (invisible) radiation is emitted. This radiation hits a special phosphor coating on the inside walls of the tube and excites the atoms in the phosphor to a higher level. When these excited electrons decay to a lower orbit in the phosphor atoms, a visible white light is emitted through the glass envelope.

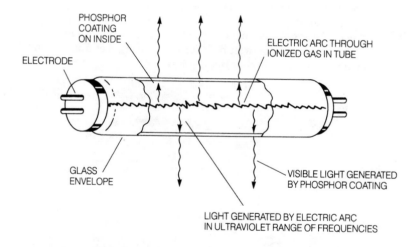

Figure 2-5. *Conversion of Electrical Energy to Light Energy Using Fluorescent Lamp*

Since the ultraviolet to visible light conversion involves direct electron excitation and energy release, this portion of the lamp operation is almost 100 percent efficient. However, some power loss occurs in the heat of the electric current passing through the inert gas in the tube and through an associated external device called the ballast. However, the loss of electrical energy to waste heat is not as big a percentage as the loss in the incandescent lamp and the overall efficiency of the fluorescent lamp is increased to about 20 percent. Gas discharge lamps also can be filled with mercury vapor or sodium vapor. These commonly are used for street lighting. These high intensity lamps also are more efficient than equivalently rated incandescent lamps.

Conversion Efficiency of Lamps

The efficiency of light sources is very important since around 24 percent of electrical energy is used for lighting. Also, lighting accounts for about 6 percent of all energy usage.

One way of expressing energy efficiency for light sources is in terms of a quantity called lumens per watt. The lumen is used to measure the amount of energy in a beam of light. Light bulb packages indicate the number of lumens available from a given bulb. The watt is used to measure electrical power and the number of watts used by the light bulb is marked on the package and the bulb itself. For example, if a 60-watt bulb is rated at 840 lumens, the conversion efficiency is 840/60, or 14 lumens per watt. The lumen output of a bulb is important because the illumination required for a given task is usually measured in terms of lumens per square foot. For example, reading or writing requires around 10 lumens per square foot.

The relationships between power and lumens/square foot are illustrated in *Figure 2-6*. In this figure, the lumens per square foot are computed for an 840-lumen, 60-watt bulb at a distance of 5 feet from the bulb. The surface area of a hemisphere at this distance is:

$$\text{Area} = 2\pi r^2$$

When r = 5 feet,

$$\text{Area} = 2\pi 5^2$$
$$= 157 \text{ sq. ft.}$$

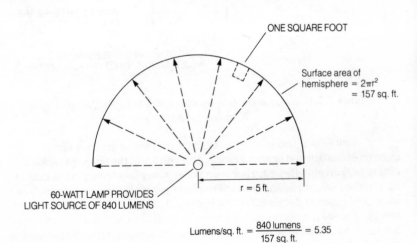

$$\text{Lumens/sq. ft.} = \frac{840 \text{ lumens}}{157 \text{ sq. ft.}} = 5.35$$

Figure 2-6. *Measure of Illumination*

This area of 157 square feet receives 840 lumens; therefore, the illumination is 840/157, or about 5 lumens per square foot. This is only enough illumination for background lighting. To read or write, either the lumens output of the bulb, thus its wattage, must be increased by 2, or the user must move closer to the bulb. Alternatively, a more efficient light source that produces twice as many lumens with the same input power could be used. This would allow reading or writing to be performed at the 5 foot distance with the same power cost.

HOW IS MECHANICAL ENERGY GENERATED?

Thermal energy, electrical energy, or chemical energy may be converted to mechanical energy through the use of several methods. Also, the kinetic energy from the flowing water released from a water reservoir or from a river may be converted to mechanical energy. All of these techniques of generating mechanical energy are related to the principle of action and reaction in physics as well as the acceleration of a material mass when a force is applied to the mass. These principles were formulated by Newton and form the basis of the behavior of classical mechanical systems.

Water Turbine

One of the early means of developing mechanical energy that is still of importance today is the use of a turbine that is driven by falling water. The energy source in this case is the force of gravity pulling the water to a lower level. The falling water may be a natural occurrence such as a mountain stream, but usually it is water released from the high level of a man-made reservoir. The early version was called a waterwheel and was often used to power machines directly. Today, the water driven turbine is used to generate mechanical energy which, in turn, is used to generate electrical energy in hydroelectric power generation plants.

In the water turbine, the potential energy of the water elevated above the turbine level is converted to kinetic energy by allowing the water to fall to the turbine (*Figure 2-7*). At the turbine level, the force of the falling water on the blades of the turbine causes the turbine shaft to rotate. Thus, the potential energy of the water is converted to kinetic mechanical energy. The rotating shaft drives a generator which converts the mechanical energy to electrical energy.

The main disadvantage of the water turbine is that a continuous flow of a large volume of water is required to provide sustained mechanical energy. This means that large reservoirs must be created in high elevations using dams. The result is a very expensive and stationary source of mechanical energy. The only practical way to make the mechanical energy available in locations where it is needed is to convert the mechanical energy from the turbine to electrical energy, then convert the electrical energy back to mechanical energy at the point of use.

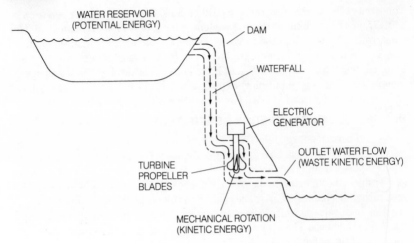

Figure 2-7. *Water Turbine Converts Potential Energy of Elevated Water into Mechanical Energy*

Steam Turbine

In the steam turbine, as shown in *Figure 2-8*, the chemical energy of a fossil fuel is converted to thermal energy to heat water. The thermal energy converts the water to a gas which we commonly call steam. As the steam flows through the turbine blades, the gas expands and cools, releasing the energy gained from the thermal energy. The pressure of the expansion causes the blades and output shaft to turn. Thus, the output shaft of the steam turbine provides mechanical energy that can be used directly or converted to electrical energy. It is interesting to note the several conversions of energy involved in the process; chemical to thermal, thermal to mechanical, mechanical to electrical.

Gas Turbine

Another approach to generating mechanical energy is to use a gas turbine. It is similar to the steam turbine in that an expanding gas produces pressure to turn the turbine. In the gas turbine (*Figure 2-9*), fuel and air (or some other source of oxygen) are burned in a combustion chamber that is integral with the turbine. In the steam turbine, combustion occurs outside the turbine and heat is exchanged to the steam. In the gas turbine the combustion occurs within the turbine itself. The thermal energy from the combustion causes expansion of the gases in the chamber. The expanding hot gas leaves the chamber and passes through the turbine blades. The gas pressure on the blades of the turbine cause the turbine to turn to produce rotational mechanical energy. A means of improving the efficiency is to compress the air before it enters the turbine. For this reason, some of the mechanical energy at the output is used to turn a compressor at the turbine input. It forces more air into the combustion chamber and compresses it for more efficient operation.

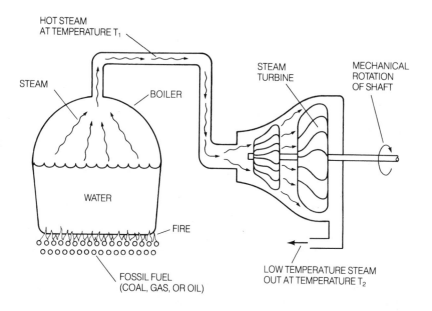

Figure 2-8. *Steam Turbine Converts Chemical Energy into Mechanical Energy*

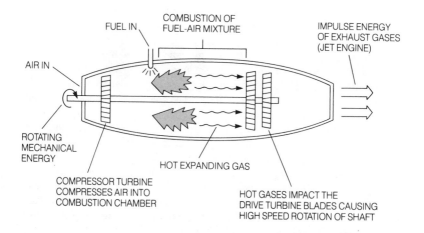

Figure 2-9. *Gas Turbine Converts Chemical Energy into Mechanical Energy*

A version of the gas turbine is the airplane turbine jet engine. The application is a bit different than the gas turbine for driving machinery or generators. Here the emphasis is on using the expanding exhaust gases for pushing to make the airplane fly. The propulsion force is provided by the reaction force of the high pressure gas leaving the exhaust nozzle of the engine. For this reason, the turbine design is different. Here a turbine with a few blades or stages is used to develop only the rotational force needed to drive the compressor, while in gas turbines used to drive vehicles or provide mechanical energy for machines, a turbine with many blades or stages is used to convert as much as possible of the gas pressure to rotational force. Any energy not converted to rotational force is wasted as heat. In the jet engine, gas expansion not converted to propulsion is wasted. Notice again that several conversions of energy are required to get mechanical from chemical.

The gas turbine has two potential advantages over a gasoline internal combustion engine (discussed later) in that the energy conversion efficiency can be higher for the turbine and it can burn a less expensive fossil fuel than that used by present gasoline engines. The gas turbine has been used only experimentally in automobile, train, or factory mechanical systems; however, it is the major source of energy for jet airplanes.

Steam Piston Engine

The steam piston engine also uses the force of expanding gas (steam) to produce mechanical energy. As in the steam turbine, the steam is produced by heating water. However, the pressure from the steam is used to push a piston connected to a crankshaft rather than turbine blades.

The high temperature and high pressure steam is let into the cylinder by a valve when the piston is at the left end of the cylinder (*Figure 2-10*). This exerts great force on the surface of the piston which pushes the piston through the cylinder and rotates the crankshaft and flywheel. At the end of the stroke, the steam pressure and temperature have been lowered due to the expansion of the gas and the conversion of the energy to mechanical movement of the piston has been completed. In some steam engines, such as used in the steam locomotive used on railroads, the exhaust steam is released from the cylinder into the atmosphere. In other types of engines, the condensed steam (water) is returned to the boiler.

The engine of *Figure 2-10* produces power on both the left and right stroke. Some steam engines produce power only on one stroke. In this case, the flywheel action or the drive from another cylinder whose piston is at the beginning of its power stroke will cause the first piston to reverse direction and move back to the starting point in its cylinder. This completes one cycle and the entire sequence of events repeats over and over. The reciprocating (side to side or up and down) motion of the piston is converted to rotary motion by the crankshaft or other mechanical linkages appropriate for the particular application.

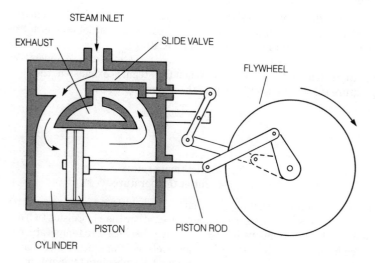

a. Steam enters left side and pushes piston to the right.
Steam on right side is forced out exhaust port.

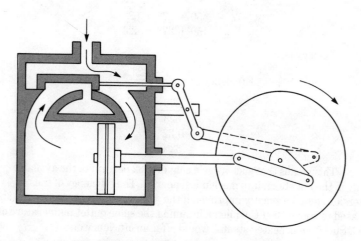

b. Steam enters right side and pushes piston to the left.
Steam on left side is forced out exhaust port.

Figure 2-10. *Basic Steam Engine*

Efficiency of the Steam Engine

The efficiency of the steam engine cycle was determined by a man named Carnot to be the difference between the inlet and outlet temperatures divided by the temperature of the inlet temperature.

Let's take an example. The inlet valve to a steam engine injects 350°C temperature steam into the cylinder. When the steam is exhausted, the temperature is 150°C. The efficiency of the steam engine is:

$$\text{Efficiency} = \frac{T_{in} - T_{out}}{T_{in}}$$

where:

$$T_{in} = \text{inlet temperature}$$
$$T_{out} = \text{outlet temperature}$$

Carnot found, however, that his equation worked only when the temperatures were referenced to absolute zero temperature rather than in Celsius (°C) or Fahrenheit (°F). 0°C temperature is 273° above absolute zero temperature measured in degrees Kelvin; therefore, any Celsius temperature must have 273° added to it to convert it to degrees Kelvin (°K), absolute temperature degrees.

For this reason, T_{in} and T_{out} are converted to °K as follows:

	°C	°K
T_{in}	350 + 273 =	623
T_{out}	150 + 273 =	423

and the efficiency is:

$$\text{Efficiency} = \frac{623 - 423}{623}$$
$$= \frac{200}{623}$$
$$= 0.32$$
$$= 32\%$$

This means that such a cycle converts 32 percent of the available energy in the hot steam into mechanical energy. The efficiency of the conversion could be greatly improved if the steam inlet temperature could be increased to above 1000°C while maintaining the same outlet temperature of 150°C. Such "superheated steam" would offer an efficiency of:

$$\text{Efficiency} = \frac{1273 - 423}{1273}$$
$$= \frac{850}{1273}$$
$$= 0.63$$
$$= 63\%$$

The use of such superheated steam can almost double the efficiency of the conversion process over that of the lower temperature steam engine. In either case, the energy that is not converted to mechanical energy is wasted as heat into the environment. Thus, in the low temperature steam engine, 68 percent of the available energy is wasted as heat which simply contributes to the thermal energy in the environment. Such waste heat in large amounts actually can have a very harmful effect on the environment. Many power generating plants with cooling ponds for discharge water from steam turbines have made extensive studies of the heating effect on the environment of fish and wildlife.

Internal Combustion Piston Engine

The steam engine is called an external combustion engine because combustion of the fuel takes place outside the cylinder. In the internal combustion engine, combustion takes place inside the cylinder. Most of us are familiar with this type of engine because it is the type used in automobiles, motorcycles, and lawnmowers. This engine converts the chemical energy in a fossil fuel into mechanical energy. The fuel is mixed with air and the combustion takes place within a cylinder in which a moveable piston is placed.

Spark-Ignited—4 Strokes per Cycle Engine

In the spark-ignited, gasoline engine, the air-fuel mixture is compressed by the piston. The compressed mixture is ignited by an electric spark from a spark plug. The burning of the air-fuel mixture creates force against the piston and forces it down.

The up and down motion of the piston is converted to rotational motion by the crankshaft. In an engine with more than one cylinder, the other pistons provide power strokes in sequence to the crankshaft to keep the energy output of the crankshaft continuous. A large mass attached to the crankshaft, called the flyweel, smooths the power pulses and supplies inertial force to keep the piston moving during any period of non-power producing strokes. The rotational mechanical energy may be used to drive vehicle wheels or factory machinery through the use of pulleys, belts, or gears.

The conversion efficiency of the gasoline engine is around 25 percent; thus, only 1/4 (25%) of the energy available in the fuel is converted to useful mechanical energy. The other 3/4 (75%) of the available energy is dissipated as waste heat into the environment.

Diesel Engine

The diesel engine operates similarly to the spark ignited gasoline engine except that extremely high compression produces enough heat to ignite the fuel and air mixture in the cylinder rather than a spark. The fuel used in the diesel engine is usually cheaper than gasoline and the diesel engine is slightly more efficient than the gasoline engine with a conversion efficiency in the 30 to 40 percent range. However, in vehicles, some of this increased efficiency may be offset by having to move the greater weight of the diesel engine. The greater weight is a result of the sturdier construction required because of the high compression in the cylinders.

Electric Motors

Most of the techniques for generating mechanical energy discussed so far have involved the conversion of thermal or mechanical potential energy into mechanical kinetic energy. One important conversion that makes much of our modern lifestyle and technology possible is the conversion of electrical energy into mechanical energy by the electric motor. Electric motors are so important that one chapter of this book is devoted to them, so we won't go into any more detail here.

Wind Turbine

The wind turbine, often called a windmill, can be used successfully to provide mechanical energy in areas where strong and dependable wind is present. The kinetic energy of the wind turns the turbine and its output shaft. The resulting mechanical energy can be used directly (e.g., to drive a water well pump) or it may be converted to electrical energy by a generator. The obvious problem is that the wind doesn't always blow when energy is required. Methods have been designed to store energy for later use to overcome this problem. The most common method is to store electrical energy from the windmill generator in rechargeable batteries.

HOW IS ELECTRICAL ENERGY GENERATED?

Electromagnetic Generators

The most common way of generating electrical energy is through the interaction of magnetic fields. Many of us have experienced the effect of magnetic fields through playing with permanent magnets or seeing the patterns of iron particles made near such a magnet (*Figure 2-11a*). The force exerted on one magnet by another, or the pattern made by the iron filings in the presence of a magnet, are physical evidence that some invisible field exists around every magnetic object.

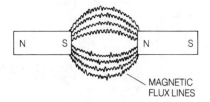

a. Flux lines between magnetic poles

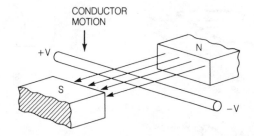

b. Voltage developed across conductor cutting magnetic flux lines

Figure 2-11. *Principle of Converting Mechanical Energy to Electrical Energy Using Magnetic Forces*

When a wire is moved so that it cuts through the lines of force of a magnetic field, a voltage is generated across the wire as shown in *Figure 2-11b*. The voltage is proportional to the rate of change of the magnetic field; that is, the faster the wire moves through the magnetic field, the greater the generated voltage. The voltage is also related to the angle at which the wire cuts the lines of force. The greatest voltage is produced when the cut is at a right angle. The voltage decreases at smaller angles until the voltage is zero when the wire is moving parallel with the lines of force. The exact same effect is produced if the wire is held stationary and the magnetic field is moved. If the wire is part of a closed circuit, current will flow through the circuit due to the generated electrical voltage.

In order to make an electrical generator, the wire is formed into a coil as shown in *Figure 2-12* and placed in a magnetic field which is set up between the poles of magnets. To provide motion to the coil, a mechanical force turns the coil at a constant speed.

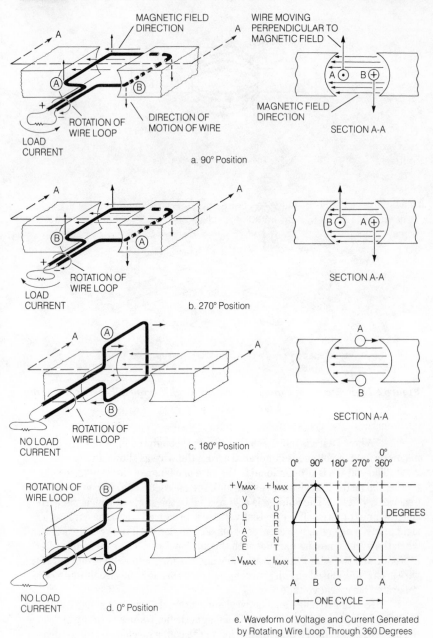

Figure 2-12. Simplified Electromagnetic Generator to Convert Mechanical Energy to Electrical Energy

The speed of the coil movement, the direction of its movement, and the angle at which it cuts the magnetic field (lines of force) determines the amount of voltage generated in the coil and the direction of current flow through the coil. As shown in *Figure 2-12a*, the direction of the motion of the conductor is at a right angle (perpendicular) to the direction of the magnetic field. The A side is moving upward and the B side is moving downward so the generated voltage causes a current to flow in the direction shown. Since the conductor is cutting across the magnetic field lines at a 90° angle, the maximum change in magnetic field occurs at this point and the maximum voltage is generated. This is shown as point B on *Figure 2-12e*. If the coil is rotated one-half turn to the 270° position, as shown in *Figure 2-12b*, then the A side of the coil and the B side of the coil have exchanged places. The coil conductor is cutting the magnetic field lines at a right angle so the voltage generated is maximum, but now the A side is moving downward and the B side is moving upward. This produces voltage in the opposite direction, as shown for point D in *Figure 2-12e* and causes current to flow in the opposite direction.

When the coil is rotated 90° from the position in *Figure 2-12a* to the 180° position, as shown in *Figure 2-12c*, the conductor is moving parallel to the magnetic field lines. Since no magnetic field lines are being cut, there is no change in magnetic field; therefore, no voltage is generated. This is shown as point C on *Figure 2-12e*. A similar condition exists, as shown in *Figure 2-12d*, when the coil sides have interchanged places because the coil is rotated to the 0° position. The conductor is again moving parallel to the magnetic field lines; therefore, the voltage again is zero (point A, *Figure 2-12e*).

Of course, the coil is rotating continuously so the voltage changes continuously as indicated by the complete waveform shown in *Figure 2-12e*. This waveform is called a sine wave because it can be represented mathematically by the sine of an angle function varying with time. This is called an alternating current because it alternately flows in one direction, then the other direction. The waveform of *Figure 2-12e* shows how the voltage and resultant circuit current vary in amplitude and direction with time in an alternating current circuit. The frequency of the alternations is dependent on the rotational speed of the coil and the number of poles (magnetic fields) in the generator.

It is possible to generate direct current (current flow in only one direction) by switching (commutating) the wire connections as the coil passes through the 180° (*Figure 2-13a*) and 0° (*Figure 2-13b*) positions (the positions where zero voltage occurs). Note that the gap in the commutator occurs as the coil passes through the zero voltage positions and that the brushes (contacts) switch the connections so that the A and B sides of the coil are interchanged with respect to the load. Since the voltage is always in the same direction even though it varies in amplitude, current flow is always in the same direction as shown in the waveform of *Figure 2-13c*.

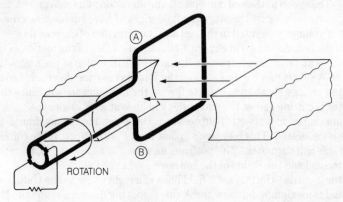

a. Brushes Switching Left Side of Load from A Side to B Side at 180° Position

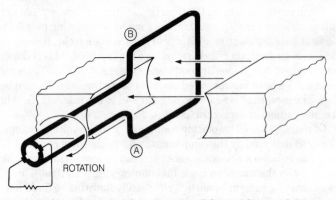

b. Brushes Switching Left Side of Load from B Side to A Side at 0° Position

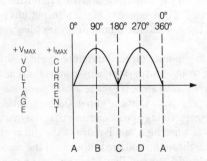

c. Direct Current Waveform Produced by Switching

***Figure 2-13.** Method to Convert AC to DC*

In both the generators of *Figure 2-12* and *Figure 2-13*, some force must be applied to the coil shaft to provide energy to rotate it in the magnetic field. At large central power plants, this energy is commonly provided by a steam turbine or a water turbine. Small local power plants may use an internal combustion engine to drive the generator. At isolated locations, a windmill may be used to drive a generator.

At some locations, it may be necessary to use an electric motor to drive the generator. For example, if only dc power is available at a location and ac power is needed, a dc motor can be used to drive an ac generator to convert the dc electrical energy to ac electrical energy. A motor-generator also may be used to change the frequency of the available ac voltage to a different frequency ac voltage. However, this is not the most efficient way to perform these conversions because certain electronic techniques can provide the same conversion with lower energy loss.

Battery

Another technique for generating electrical energy is to convert it directly from chemical energy. Through the combination of materials and chemical reactions, electrical energy becomes the output of chemical energy inputs. The battery is a good example of this process.

Some batteries are rechargeable and some are not. A rechargeable battery is recharged by forcing current from an external generator through the battery in the reverse direction. This reverses the chemical reactions, and stores the electrical energy from the charging current in the battery.

For example, let's consider the rechargeable battery used in automobiles. Its primary purpose is to provide electrical energy to the electric starter motor to start the automobile engine. When the engine is running, part of its mechanical energy turns an electric generator to recharge the battery and to provide the electrical energy for the accessory electrical equipment on the automobile.

The basic structure of the lead-acid battery used on the automobile is shown in *Figure 2-14*. It consists of a negative electrode, positive electrode and a sulphuric acid solution called the electrolyte. The negative electrode is a lead plate made so that a large surface area is exposed to the electrolyte. The chemical reaction of the lead with the sulfuric acid produces a lead sulfate coating on the lead plate and generates hydrogen ions. This causes the lead electrode to be negative because positive lead ions are drawn into solution by the acid leaving behind electrons that are supplied to an external closed circuit. These electrons move through the external circuit as part of the current flow. At the positive electrode, the hydrogen ions pull electrons from the lead oxide leaving the lead oxide with a positive potential. It is the release of the electrons, the forming of ions in solution, and the movement of the electrons from one electrode to the other through the external circuit that provides the electrical energy.

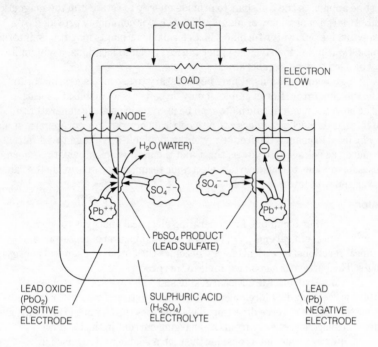

Figure 2-14. *Conversion of Chemical Energy to Electrical Energy with the Lead-Acid Storage Cell*

The chemical reaction produces an electrical voltage of about 2 volts per pair of plates. Higher battery terminal voltages are obtained by connecting pairs of plates so that the negative electrode of one pair is connected to the positive electrode of the next pair. This is called a series connection because the same current is flowing through each plate pair. The amount of current that the battery can deliver is related to the area of the plates. Connecting plates in parallel increases the effective plate area; thus, the current delivery capability.

Although other types of batteries use different materials for the electrodes and a different electrolyte solution, some of which are not liquid (dry-cell), the general process is the same as described for the lead-acid battery.

Fuel Cell

Another type of chemical to electrical energy conversion takes place in a device known as a fuel cell. The basic operation of this device is similar to a battery except the chemical agents involved are typically gases instead of liquids. The hydrogen-oxygen fuel cell is illustrated in *Figure 2-15*. The cell consists of a source of hydrogen gas which flows into the cathode region of the cell (the negative electrode) and a source of oxygen which flows into the anode region (the positive electrode). In between these two electrodes is an ion exchange membrane or electrolyte. The electrodes must be made of a material that will assist the chemical reactions that are to take place. Such materials are called catalysts.

The purpose of the ion exchange membrane is to separate the hydrogen atoms into positively charged hydrogen ions (hydrogen atoms without their electrons) and electrons. The electrons from the hydrogen atoms are collected by the cathode material and pass through the external circuit as current flow. The positively charged hydrogen ions pass through the membrane or electrolyte to the anode. The electrons returning from the external circuit flow into the anode electrode material and combine with the hydrogen ions and the oxygen to produce water. The output voltage from such a cell when it has no load is typically over 1 volt, but when loaded at normal load currents, it is between 0.5 and 1 volt. The conversion efficiency is over 50 percent (conversion of available chemical energy to electrical energy).

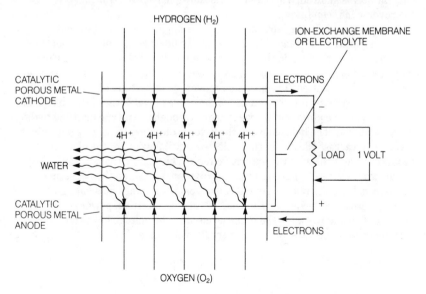

Figure 2-15. *Chemical to Electrical Energy Conversion Using a Fuel Cell*
(Source: E. M. Walsh, Energy Conversion, *Ronald Press, 1967)*

There are high temperature and low temperature fuel cells. Cells that operate at temperatures below 300 degrees Celsius are classified as low temperature cells. Low temperature cells require relatively pure sources of hydrogen and oxygen, but high temperature cells can use hydrocarbon fuels and air. These are broken down into hydrogen and carbon monoxide and air to provide the basic fuel cell reactions. Fuel cells have been very useful in providing electrical power for space ships as well as water for astronauts. Their use on earth has been limited, but the fuel cell could find significant future applications for energy conversion if the reliability and operation of these devices are improved.

Photovoltaic Diode

Solar energy can be converted directly into electrical energy by the photovoltaic diode, commonly called a solar cell. Such devices have been used extensively to provide electrical power for communications satellites that orbit the earth. The basic operation of this conversion process can be explained by looking at the structure of a semiconductor diode shown in *Figure 2-16*. This type of device freely passes current when a positive voltage is applied to the anode and a negative voltage is applied to the cathode. This condition is shown in *Figure 2-16a* and is called the forward bias condition. When the applied voltage polarity is reversed; that is, when a negative voltage is applied to the anode and a positive voltage is applied to the cathode, only a minute amount of current flow is allowed. This condition is shown in *Figure 2-16b* and is called the reverse bias condition.

When visible or infrared radiation is applied to the p-type material, as shown in *Figures 2-16c* and *2-17*, a current can flow because of the generation of electrons free to move in the p-region even with no voltage applied. Current flow occurs because electron-hole pairs are formed due to the energy received from the light radiation. The basic conversion is illustrated in *Figure 2-17*. The light energy striking an electron raises the energy level of the electron enough to free it from the atom so it is free to move through the p-type material to the n-type material. The holes move in the reverse direction. If an external circuit is connected across the diode, these electrons will flow out of the diode to produce current through the external circuit. The voltage that appears across the diode and the external circuit (the load) is dependent on the resistance in the external circuit. When light energy develops a forward bias voltage polarity across the diode (see *Figure 2-16c* again), electrical power is generated and delivered to the external circuit. The voltage levels for which such conditions exist are very low, in the 0.5 volt range.

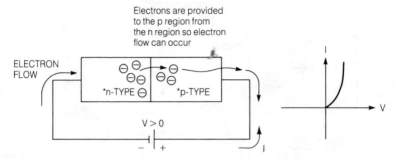

Electrons are provided
to the p region from
the n region so electron
flow can occur

*n-type has extra electrons
*p-type has insufficient electrons

a. Forward Bias Condition

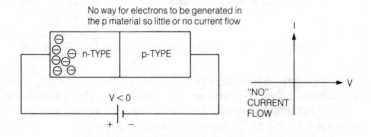

No way for electrons to be generated in
the p material so little or no current flow

b. Reverse Bias Condition

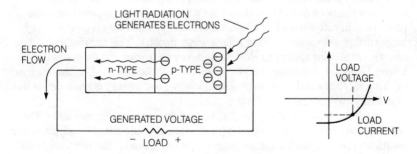

c. Light Illumination Condition

Figure 2-16. *Photovoltaic Diode Operation*

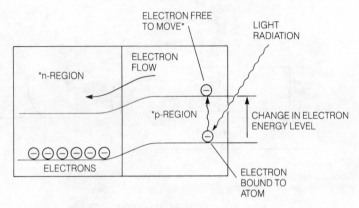

*Electrons flow into electron deficient regions from electron rich regions much as ink
in water tends to spread from the ink rich spot where it is introduced to portions of
water containing no ink.

Figure 2-17. *Basic Mechanism of Photoelectric Conversion*

The current produced per square unit of diode area is also quite small
so that a large surface area is required to generate even low power levels. For
example, a square meter of diode surface area might produce over 100
amperes at 0.5 volt for a total power output of 50 watts (50 watts per square
meter) when the solar radiation density is 1000 watts per square meter. Thus,
conversion efficiency is only 5 percent; that is, only 5 percent of the available
solar energy is converted to electrical energy. This very low conversion
efficiency has been one of the difficulties with this conversion method in the
past. To generate even a few kilowatts of energy in this way requires a very
large surface area and/or higher solar energy density. This has made direct
conversion of solar energy to electrical energy too expensive for general
usage. However, the present high cost can be justified for applications such as
orbiting satellites and space exploration where solar energy is more dense and
alternate power sources are not practical.

The structure of *Figure 2-18* is used for non-rotating satellites. The
solar cells are mounted on large flat panels that are automatically adjusted to a
position to receive the maximum solar radiation. Even for the relatively small
satellite power requirements (in the kilowatt range), over a hundred square
meters of panel area may be required.

A problem using solar energy for homes has been the storage of the
energy in the daytime during sunlight for use at peak periods at night. New
techniques, which will be discussed in a later chapter, are being applied to
these problems so that residential use may be practical in the future.

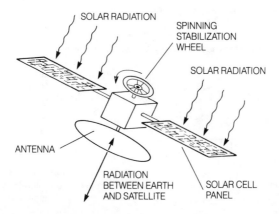

Figure 2-18. *Solar Cells on Satellites*
(Source: D.L. Cannon and G. Luecke, Understanding Communications Systems,
Texas Instruments Inc., 1980)

WHAT HAVE WE LEARNED?

1. The principle forms of energy that are useful to us are thermal, light, mechanical, and electrical.

2. Thermal energy for space heating and industrial processes is obtained primarily from the combustion of fossil fuels and secondarily from the conversion of electrical energy into heat.

3. Light energy for building and street lighting requirements is primarily obtained from electrical energy.

4. Mechanical energy for transportation, industry, and other activities is primarily obtained by converting chemical energy to thermal energy by combustion, then converting the thermal energy into mechanical energy through the use of engines. A secondary source of mechanical energy is obtained through electric motors which convert electrical energy into mechanical energy. The kinetic energy of wind and falling water also may be converted to mechanical energy.

5. Electrical energy is primarily converted from mechanical energy by electromagnetic generators. A less important source of electrical energy is through the conversion of chemical or solar radiation energy directly into electrical form. Electrical energy is very useful because it may be transported easily and quickly over long distances. Then it can be readily converted to the needed form of energy at the use location.

Quiz for Chapter 2

1. Most energy is used in the final form of:
   a. thermal
   b. electrical
   c. mechanical
   d. light

2. Most of the energy used is supplied by:
   a. direct solar radiation
   b. wood
   c. fossil fuels
   d. nuclear energy

3. Light energy is generated by:
   a. nuclear reaction on the sun
   b. changes in the energy levels of electrons
   c. friction in mechanical systems
   d. all of the above
   e. a and b above
   d. a and c above

4. Which of the following is a unit of light efficiency?
   a. lumens
   b. lumens/watt
   c. watts/lumens
   d. watts

5. A 100-watt bulb providing 1000 lumens has what light efficiency?
   a. 1
   b. 10
   c. 100
   d. 1,000

6. If a person is reading at a distance of 10 feet from a light, how many lumens (nearest 1,000) must the light produce?
   a. 1,000
   b. 2,000
   c. 4,000
   d. 6,000

7. A 40-watt fluorescent bulb will produce approximately the same number of lumens as a typical incandescent bulb of how many watts?
   a. 40
   b. 160
   c. 200
   d. 250

8. If a steam cycle uses a hot steam temperature of 1,000 degrees Celsius and an outlet steam temperature of 400 degrees Celsius, what is the efficiency in percent of the cycle?
   a. 25
   b. 47
   c. 54
   d. 70

9. If a mass of 1 millionth of a kilogram is converted completely to energy, how many kilowatt-hours of energy would be generated?
   a. 2,500
   b. 8,530
   c. 25,000
   d. 90,000

10. If a photovoltaic diode's conversion efficiency is 5% and the solar radiation density is 1,500 watts/meter^2, how many square meters of solar cells would be required to produce 10 kilowatts of power?
    a. 10
    b. 100
    c. 133
    d. 250

11. A fuel cell uses:
    a. chemical reactions between metal electrodes and a liquid or paste to produce electrical energy
    b. chemical reactions between an oxidant gas and a hydrogen rich material or chemical to produce electrical energy
    c. neither of the above

12. A wire is moving through a magnetic field with a certain velocity. If the velocity is doubled, the generated voltage is:
    a. halved
    b. doubled
    c. no change

Electronic Control Functions

ABOUT THIS CHAPTER

Many of the techniques used for the electronic control of energy require a basic understanding of electronic functions and how they are used in control systems. Therefore, the fundamentals of analog functions, digital functions, control system structures and operation, and microcomputer control systems will be covered in this chapter.

ANALOG SIGNALS AND FUNCTIONS

Control systems traditionally have used a form of electrical signal whose level varies continually with time. This type of signal, illustrated in *Figure 3-1*, is called an analog signal. It is the type of signal that has been most frequently encountered in electronic and electrical systems. For example, the audio (music and speech) signals in radio and stereo systems are analog. So are the audio and video signals in television. They tend to be random as shown in *Figure 3-1a*. The electrical power delivered to homes and factories also is analog. It is a continually varying sinusoid as shown in *Figure 3-1b*. This waveform is just like the generator waveform of *Figure 2-12e*.

Periodic Waves

The sinusoid is a periodic (repeating) waveform with a waveshape described by the mathematical sine function. A periodic waveform repeats once every T seconds, with T being the period of the waveform in seconds. The reciprocal of the period (1/T) is the frequency in cycles per second or hertz. A signal that has a period of one second has a frequency of one hertz. Analog signals are not always periodic and may be periodic without being a pure sinusoid. A periodic analog signal is actually a combination of a large number of sinusoids of differing frequencies and amplitudes.

One way of expressing the amplitude (level) of the sine wave of *Figure 3-1b* is to measure the maximum positive or negative value of the voltage or current that the waveform represents. This is called the peak value. Analog voltages that are not symmetrical around the axis (*Figure 3-1a*) have separate positive and negative peak values. The sinusoid also has a root-mean-square (rms) value that is used to express its amplitude. It can be calculated easily by dividing the peak value by 1.414, (the square root of 2). The non-sinusoidal analog waveform also has an rms value, but its relationship to the peak value is not as simple as that of the sinusoid.

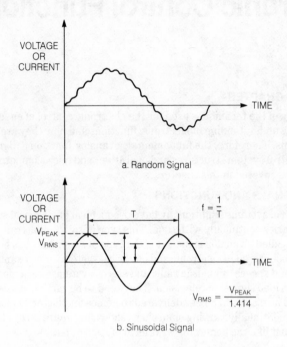

Figure 3-1. *Analog Signals*

Amplification

Any analog device that processes analog signals (performs an analog function) must preserve the shape of the signal unless the intention is to alter the shape in a predetermined way. The simplest analog function is that of amplification as shown in *Figure 3-2*. This function, performed by a circuit called an amplifier, simply multiplies the amplitude of the analog waveform by a constant, k. The shape of the waveform versus time is not changed, but the output waveform is larger in amplitude than the input signal.

This is an important function in all electronic systems because many signal inputs are very weak and must be boosted to levels that have enough voltage, current or power amplitude to drive other devices in the system. For example, the signal from a phonograph needle in a music system is very small, in the range of one or two one-thousandths of a volt. In order to provide enough power to drive a loudspeaker so the music can be heard, the signal from the phonograph must be boosted or amplified at least one thousand times. The amplification is usually performed by one or more electronic amplifier circuits connected between the phonograph cartridge and the loudspeaker.

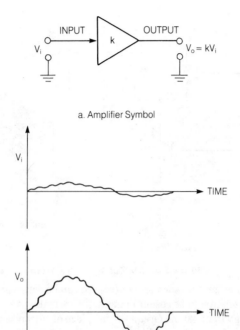

a. Amplifier Symbol

b. Waveforms

Figure 3-2. *Amplification*

Amplification also is used in electronic control systems where the weak signal from a system sensor has to be amplified to the levels needed to drive motors, relays, and other system control elements. A sensor is a device that converts a physical value such as temperature or speed into an electrical signal (voltage or current) so it can be processed by the electronic circuits in the control system.

INTEGRATED CIRCUITS

Figure 3-3a illustrates an electronic amplifier circuit. It is a differential amplifier. A very small difference between input voltages V_1 and V_2 can cause a very large voltage change in V_o. The voltage difference at the inputs is amplified to the voltage, V_o, at the output. The voltages V_1 and V_2 are applied to the bases of transistors Q_1 and Q_2 and, since the transistor is a device that draws little input current to control a large output current, the currents required from the input voltage sources V_1 and V_2 are very small.

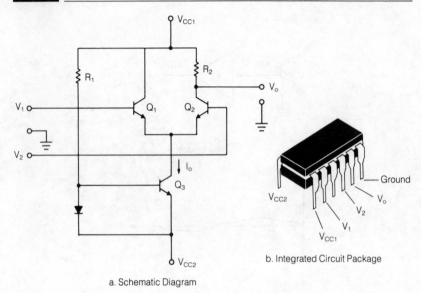

a. Schematic Diagram

b. Integrated Circuit Package

Figure 3-3. *Basic Amplifier Circuit*

Amplifier circuits such as *Figure 3-3a* can be constructed by using individual components, but present manufacturers make use of integrated circuit technology to make the circuit on one piece of silicon so that the circuit can be purchased in a small plastic or ceramic package as shown in *Figure 3-3b*.

The IC Process

An integrated circuit is commonly referred to by its abbreviation, IC. A brief summary of the process steps is shown in *Figure 3-4*. The process begins with a polished round disk of pure crystalline silicon material. Certain areas of the silicon surface, which are selected by a photographic process, are modified by diffusing impurities into the surface to form resistors, transistors and diodes in a repeated pattern as shown in *Figure 3-4a*. Aluminum metallization is evaporated over the complete slice and some of it is removed selectively. The remaining metallization provides conductive paths that interconnect the complete circuit. All components are manufactured in steps and the matrix of *Figure 3-4a* shows that hundreds are made at the same time. The individual circuits could be a complex logic subsystem or a complete integrated circuit amplifier. When cut apart with a diamond scribe, the individual chips can fit on the tip of a finger as shown in *Figure 3-4b*.

Each chip is mounted on a metallized frame that supports it and provides the means for connecting the circuit into a system. The circuit connections on the chip are bonded to the metallized frame with 1 mil [0.001 inch (2.5 mm)] wires so the electrical connections can be made through the package pins as shown in *Figure 3-4c*.

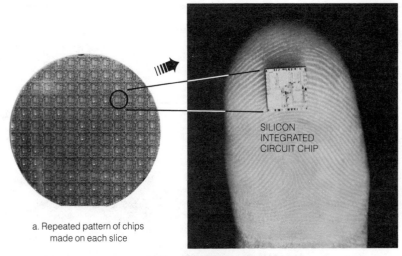

a. Repeated pattern of chips made on each slice

SILICON INTEGRATED CIRCUIT CHIP

b. Individual chips cut apart

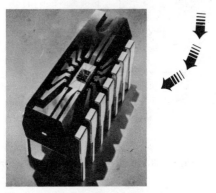

c. Each chip packaged separately

***Figure 3-4.** Integrated Circuit Process*

Operational Amplifiers

An extremely versatile electronic amplifier that is available in integrated circuit form and has a very high voltage gain and very low input currents is called an operational amplifier. The operational amplifier can be used to perform many kinds of functions used in control circuits.

Figures 3-5 and *3-6* show some of the common functions that operational amplifiers can perform. The basic amplifier is represented by the triangular symbol shown in *Figure 3-5a*. The input marked with the plus sign is called the non-inverting input and the input marked with the minus sign is the inverting input. A voltage going more positive applied to the minus input would produce an output voltage that is 180° out of phase; it would go negative.

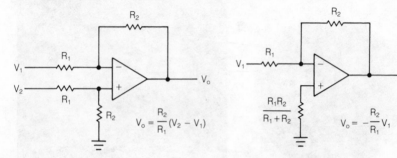

a. Differential Amplifier

$$V_o = -\frac{R_2}{R_1}(V_2 - V_1)$$

b. Single-Ended Amplifier

$$V_o = -\frac{R_2}{R_1}V_1$$

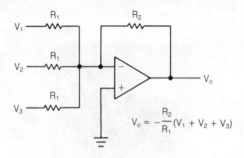

$$V_o = -\frac{R_2}{R_1}(V_1 + V_2 + V_3)$$

c. Summing Amplifier

Figure 3-5. *Operational Amplifier Functions*

The circuit of *Figure 3-5a* is a differential amplifier just like *Figure 3-3a*. Note that the gain (the k factor of *Figure 3-2*) is determined by $\frac{R_2}{R_1}$, the ratio of resistors R_1 and R_2. R_2 is called the feedback resistor because it feeds back part of the output signal to the input. R_1 is the input resistor. Thus, the gain can be set easily by choosing the values of these resistors. With the gain set by the resistors, the amplifier will produce an output voltage that is a closely controlled multiple of the difference between V_1 and V_2.

A single-ended amplifier connected as an inverting amplifier is shown in *Figure 3-5b*. In this case, the output voltage is the ratio of R_2 over R_1 times the inverted input voltage V_1. The minus sign in the equation indicates that the output signal is inverted. A single-ended, inverting, summing amplifier connection is shown in *Figure 3-5c*. In this case, the output voltage is the ratio of R_2 over R_1 times the inverted, algebraic sum of the voltages V_1, V_2, and V_3.

Filters are used to pass wanted signals and reject unwanted signals or to shape signals for easy use. The low- and high-pass filter functions can be implemented using an operational amplifier with resistors and capacitors connected as shown in *Figures 3-6a* and *3-6b*. The cut-off frequencies are related to the RC products.

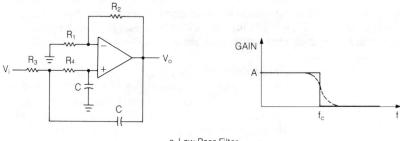

a. Low-Pass Filter

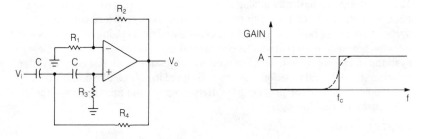

b. High-Pass Filter

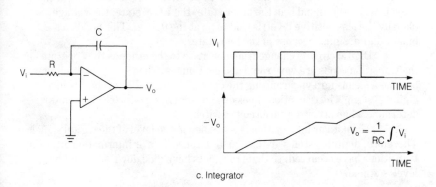

$$V_o = \frac{1}{RC} \int V_i$$

c. Integrator

Figure 3-6. *Operational Amplifier Functions*

These two filters are called second-order Butterworth filters. Their frequency response has a fairly sharp cut-off for frequencies above (low-pass) or below (high-pass) the cut-off frequency. Unwanted signals are not passed above the f_c for the low-pass filters, and below the f_c for the high-pass filters. Higher order Butterworth filters with sharper cut-off characteristics can be made by placing two or more of these type filter circuits in series. Similarly, band-pass or band-reject filters can be designed by using a low-pass filter of the type shown in *Figure 3-6a* in series with a high-pass filter of the type shown in *Figure 3-6b* when appropriate cut-off frequencies are chosen for each filter.

Some systems need a smoothing or integration function. It is implemented in simple systems with a circuit as shown in *Figure 3-6c*. In this circuit, the output voltage is the integral of V_i (area under the input voltage curve) times one divided by the product of the R and C values. The output is 180° out of phase from the input. Exchanging the positions of R and C in *Figure 3-6c* will produce a simple circuit that performs the opposite function from the integrator. It is called a differentiator.

All of the functions discussed so far have been analog signal functions. Many systems are basically analog in nature and many control systems have been constructed from analog circuits. However, many modern control systems are being built using digital functions and digital computers. This is because powerful digital functions corresponding to subsystems or total logic systems can be obtained in single circuit packages at reasonable cost. In order to understand digital functions, the digital signal itself must be understood. Let's look at some of the properties of digital signals and functions, and their relationships to analog signals.

DIGITAL SIGNALS

Digital signals have two states identified by one of two levels of voltage or current. Voltage levels are most common. When the signal is in the HIGH state, the voltage (usually the more positive level) is said to be at the 1 level. When the signal is in the other state, the LOW state, the voltage (usually the less positive level) is said to be at the 0 level. This is called a binary digital signal because of the two states.

Digital circuits change from one state to the other as they operate and the transition times are very rapid and continuous. The rapid transition times become a means for synchronizing the operation of the digital circuits in a digital system. The transition times of some digital circuits (clock circuits) determine when other digital circuits switch.

The data or information is contained in the level of the digital signals. Therefore, digital systems are designed to sense data or information after the transitions have occurred, so that transients have died down and the 1 or 0 level is stable.

Digital Signal Levels

The general form of digital signals is illustrated in *Figure 3-7*. *Figure 3-7a* shows a digital signal occurring on a single wire over a period of time with a pattern of signal levels of 1 0 1. A pattern such as this is often called a digital code and each digit is called a bit. The example would be called a 3-bit code. To detect the digital code, the system receiving the signal must sample the voltage on the wire at particular times. The times are in the center of the 0 and 1 level periods so that the signals are stable when the sample is taken. It is important to notice that the exact voltage level of the signal is not as important as whether the voltage is within the range considered to be the 1 level or within the range considered to be the 0 level. For a given type of circuit, these ranges are built into the design of the circuit. The voltage ranges shown in *Figure 3-7a* are for a popular digital circuit type known as TTL (transistor-transistor-logic). In this type of circuit, the 1 level is considered to be any voltage level greater than 1.4 volts, and it is typically 2.4 volts. The 0 level is considered to be any voltage level below 1.4 volts, and it is typically 0.2 to 0.4 volt.

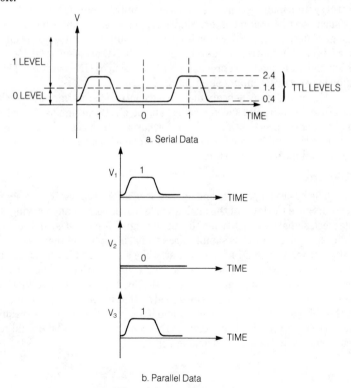

Figure 3-7. Digital Signals

Serial and Parallel Data

The digital data shown in *Figure 3-7a* is a series of bits having 0 and 1 levels occurring in time on a single wire. The bits arrive in sequence one at a time at any point on a signal line between circuits or between systems. When digital information is moved in this way, it is called *serial* digital data. The alternative to this arrangement is to provide a separate wire for each bit of a particular group of bits. Then all 0's and 1's of a given group of bits are sent between circuits or between systems at the same time as shown in *Figure 3-7b*. This is called *parallel* digital data. The same 3-bit code, 1 0 1, of *Figure 3-7a* is sent, but now it is sent in one-third the time because all bits arrive at the destination at the same time. However, it takes three times the number of wires and possibly that many times the number of circuits to handle the signals in parallel form. Thus, digital systems that handle information serially usually are less expensive and slower than systems that handle information in parallel.

CONVERSIONS, CODES AND NUMBER SYSTEMS

The 0 and 1 digital signals can be used in the action outputs required in control systems. Many control actions are simply turning ON or OFF some device such as a motor or a heater. Similarly, in processing information to make logical decisions, the decision is either yes (or true) or it is no (or false). Thus, a 0 is used in control systems to represent a NO decision or OFF condition and a 1 is used to represent a YES decision or ON condition. This situation may occur for inputs or outputs.

However, many sensors measuring control system variables such as temperature, position and speed produce analog electrical signals. In order for a digital system to process this analog information, the analog signals must be converted to their digital equivalent. This is done with a circuit called an analog-to-digital (A/D) converter.

A/D Converter

The basic components and operation of an A/D converter are shown in *Figure 3-8*. Since the level of the analog waveform is continually varying, the sample clock signal specifies when the analog signal is measured and converted to its digital equivalent. This sample clock signal is applied to the base of a field-effect transistor (FET). The FET acts like a switch and, when it is turned on by the sample clock, it connects the analog voltage to the holding capacitor and amplifier. The holding capacitor holds the level of the analog voltage value between samples. The amplifier is designed so that it doesn't significantly affect the voltage held by the capacitor and it supplies the drive level required by the A/D converter. The converter, in this case, outputs a 3-bit digital code that corresponds to the sampled analog voltage.

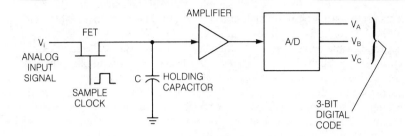

a. Circuit

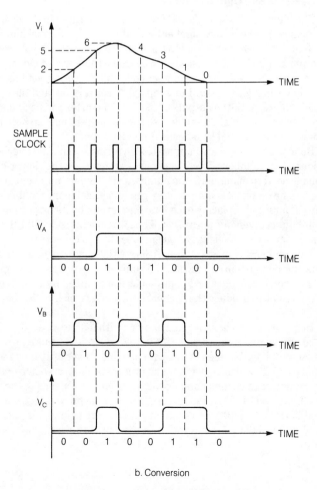

b. Conversion

Figure 3-8. *Analog-to-Digital Conversion*

In *Figure 3-8b*, the first sampled value of the analog signal is 2 volts. This produces a 3-bit parallel digital code of 010. The 010 remains at the output of the A/D converter until the next sample pulse. When the next sample pulse occurs, the analog voltage has changed to 5 volts and the A/D converter outputs a 3-bit parallel digital code of 101. This process of sampling and converting continues for the analog voltage levels of 6, 4, 3, 1 and 0 with corresponding digital code values of 110, 100, 011, 001, and 000. In such an A/D converter, the sampling rate can't be any faster than the A/D circuits can make the conversion, but must be at least twice the highest frequency that occurs in the input signal in order to preserve the fidelity of the signal.

Number Systems and Digital Codes

The digital codes that the A/D converter generated in the example of *Figure 3-8* happen to be binary number equivalents of the decimal numbers 2, 5, 6, 4, 3, 1, and 0 which correspond to the actual analog voltage values at the input. (The output doesn't necessarily always have this correspondence.) The relation between a four-bit binary number code and the corresponding decimal number is shown in *Figure 3-9a*. For simple A/D conversion (and the opposite D/A conversion process), the outputs of the A/D converter can be understood by referring to such a table. The table also shows the relationship between four-bit binary numbers and hexadecimal numbers.

Binary codes often are summarized in terms of their hexadecimal or decimal equivalent numbers for convenience and to reduce the chance of error when humans need to manipulate the numbers. The binary number can be converted to a hexadecimal equivalent by grouping the binary number digits into groups of four and replacing each four-digit group by its hexadecimal equivalent digit as given in *Figure 3-9a*. Thus, the binary code 00110110 can be written more simply as the hexadecimal number 36. To convert the hexadecimal number 36 (often written as 36_{16} with the subscript denoting the base of the number system), to its decimal equivalent involves the simple computation shown in *Figure 3-9b*. The 3 of 36 is multiplied by 16 and the 6 is added to the result to produce the decimal number 54 (which could be written as 54_{10}).

In general, for a hexadecimal number with n digits $d_n d_{n-1} d_{n-2} \ldots d_1 d_0$, the decimal equivalent is the sum of $d_n \times 16^n$ plus $d_{n-1} \times 16^{n-1}$ plus $d_{n-2} \times 16^{n-2}$ plus the rest of the digits times their corresponding power of 16 down to $d_1 \times 16^1$ and $d_0 \times 16^0$ (which is just d_0). The process is illustrated in *Figure 3-9c* for the four-digit hexadecimal number 13E8 (which corresponds to the binary number 0001 0011 1110 1000). In this case, the decimal number is $1 \times 4096 + 3 \times 256 + 14 \times 16 + 8 = 5096_{10}$. These conversions are helpful in summarizing the parallel or serial digital (binary) data that occurs in various portions of a digital system.

Binary (Base 2) Code	Decimal (Base 10) Equivalent	Hexadecimal (Base 16) Equivalent
0000	0	0
0001	1	1
0010	2	2
0011	3	3
0100	4	4
0101	5	5
0110	6	6
0111	7	7
1000	8	8
1001	9	9
1010	10	A
1011	11	B
1100	12	C
1101	13	D
1110	14	E
1111	15	F

a. Binary Code Values

$$(0011\ 0110)_2 = (36)_{16} = (3 \times 16 + 6)_{10} = 54_{10}$$

b. Conversion of an 8-Bit Unsigned Binary Number to its Decimal and Hexadecimal Equivalents

$$(d_3\ d_2\ d_1\ d_0)_{16} = (d_3 \times 4096 + d_2 \times 256 + d_1 \times 16 + d_0)_{10}$$

$$(1\ 3\ E\ 8)_{16} = (1 \times 4096 + 3 \times 256 + 14 \times 16 + 8)_{10} = 5096_{10}$$

c. Conversion of 4-digit Hexadecimal Number to its Decimal Number Equivalent

Figure 3-9. *Number Codes*

The binary code may represent the actual input analog value if it is the output of an A/D converter of the type shown in *Figure 3-8*. However, binary codes can be used to represent almost anything. An n-bit code can have 2^n different combinations which can represent 2^n different numbers or 2^n different commands, and so on. For example, an 8-bit binary code can have 256 different combinations. These can represent the decimal numbers from 0 to 255 or the decimal numbers from -128 to $+127$. (Note that the zero is a significant number in digital systems.) The 8-bit code also could represent one of 256 different instructions, or commands, or system locations depending on the meaning and use of the code. There are standard codes that are used to represent alphabetical and numerical characters and typewriter control keys. One such code is the ASCII alphanumeric code. While a simple control system may not utilize all of these different types of binary code interpretations, complex computer control centers probably would.

D/A Converter

Once a control system has processed information in digital form, it may have to convert the resulting digital code into analog form to provide some linear or proportional control operation, such as positioning a valve or machine part. The opposite of the A/D conversion must be used.

Figure 3-10 illustrates the digital-to-analog (D/A) conversion. Some form of digital signal storage holds the digital code to be converted onto the D/A circuit input. The D/A converts this value to its analog equivalent. Each time the digital code changes, the D/A output voltage changes by a certain value, causing a stairstep pattern on the output of the D/A circuit. The stairstep effect can be removed by passing this signal through a low-pass filter with an appropriate cut-off frequency. For example, if the digital codes are placed on the D/A converter at the rate of 8,000 times per second, and they represent audio speech with a frequency content of up to 4,000 hertz, a low-pass filter with a 4,000 hertz cut-off frequency would recover the desired speech waveform. The filtering may not be required at this point if the system receiving the D/A output has the appropriate filtering built into its circuits.

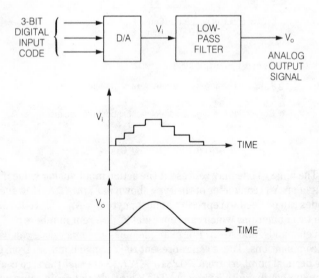

Figure 3-10. *Digital-to-Analog Conversion*

DIGITAL FUNCTIONS

Logic Gates

Once the information is inside the control system in digital form, it must be processed using digital functions. The basic digital functions are performed by devices called gates as shown in *Figure 3-11*. *Figure 3-11a* shows the symbol and operation of the AND gate function. An AND gate produces an output of 1 only if *all* inputs are at the 1 level. This function is used to make a decision for an action only if all input conditions are true. *Figure 3-11b* shows another important digital operation and symbol, that of the OR gate. The OR gate has a 1 output if *any* input has a 1. This gate provides a decision for an action if any given input condition is met.

An example of the use of the AND and OR functions in a control system would be control logic involved in a building heating system in which heat flow is individually controlled for each room in the building. If room 1 OR room 2 OR room 3 needs heat, the central heating element or furnace is turned on. Then, if the room temperature is lower than the thermostat setting AND if the furnace duct temperature has reached an acceptable level, the blower is turned on to deliver heat to the room.

Another basic digital function illustrated in *Figure 3-11c* is the eXclusive-OR (XOR) gate. This gate provides an output of 1 only if the inputs are at different logical levels. This type of gate is used in logical comparison operations to see if two digital codes have the same bit pattern or not.

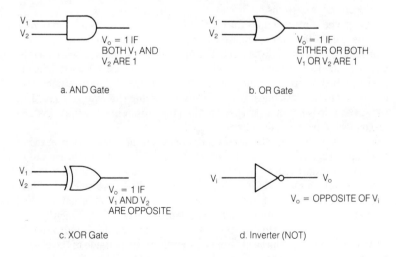

Figure 3-11. Basic Digital Functions

The final basic digital function is the inverter as shown in *Figure 3-11d*. This function provides a digital output level that is the inversion (opposite) of the input signal level. This function is called a NOT function. The inverter is used primarily to provide the proper logic level to the input of the next function. For example, if an AND gate is used to make a decision so that the output of the AND gate is 1, and the next logical function requires a 0 input for correct operation, an inverter would be required between the two functions. In fact, this operation of an AND gate followed by an inverter is available in integrated circuit form as a NAND (NOT-AND) gate, since it is commonly used in many digital systems. A NOR (NOT-OR) gate also is available.

Storage Devices

The functions of *Figure 3-11* provide the heart of the decision making in all digital systems. However, there also must be a means of storing digital codes so that devices such as D/A converters and logic gates can operate on the codes. Storage devices exist for a single bit, a group of bits, or for arrays of bits, to satisfy the various requirements of a system.

Flip-Flop

The single-bit storage cell is known as a flip-flop. One particular type, called the D flip-flop, is shown in *Figure 3-12a*. A storage device that contains several flip-flops for storage of a group of bits simultaneously, known as a register, is shown in *Figure 3-12b*. Also illustrated in *Figures 3-12b* and *3-13* is the concept of a three-state buffer commonly used with such registers in microcomputer systems.

The control signals for the flip-flop, and by extension, the register, include the D (data) input and a clock input. Note that the clock input is identified by the triangle symbol. The outputs of the register are controlled by a signal called an output enable, which controls an electronic switch inside the register. If the output enable is in its true state, the register outputs are connected to the data lines A, B, C, D in the example of *Figure 3-12b*. If the output enable is not in its true state, then the output lines of the register are disconnected from the data lines.

The clock signal controls the time when the information on the flip-flop or register inputs is stored into the flip-flop cells. In the case of *Figure 3-12*, the storage occurs when the clock signal makes a transition from the low level (0) to the high level (1). This transition is called a positive or leading-edge trigger. (There are also flip-flops or registers that store information when the high-to-low level transition occurs. This transition is called a negative or trailing-edge trigger. On register or flip-flop symbols, this is indicated by a downward arrow on the clock input or a circle on the outside of the clock input.) A 1 on the D input will produce a 1 at the Q output after a clock transition. Q will be a 0 if D = 0. The truth table describes every output condition for every input condition.

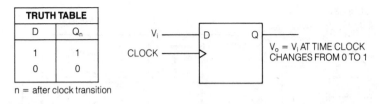

a. Single D Flip-Flop

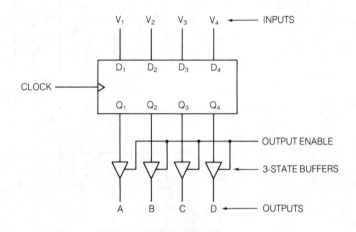

b. 3-state Output 4-Bit Register

Figure 3-12. *Flip-Flop and Register Storage of Digital Codes*

Control systems using a digital computer require the storage of many digital codes. Some of these codes represent data for the system and other codes represent the computer program that governs the control system behavior. To provide such storage with many registers of the type of *Figure 3-12* would be expensive and require a lot of physical space; therefore, a special digital circuit called a memory is used to provide such storage.

Random Access Memory

The memory circuit used for storage of system data is the random access memory (RAM). The basic structure of a static RAM type of memory is shown in *Figure 3-13*. It consists of an array of flip-flops. The number of columns (flip-flops per row) in the array defines the number of bits, n, stored per location or address. The number of rows in the array defines the number of n-bit codes that can be stored by the memory.

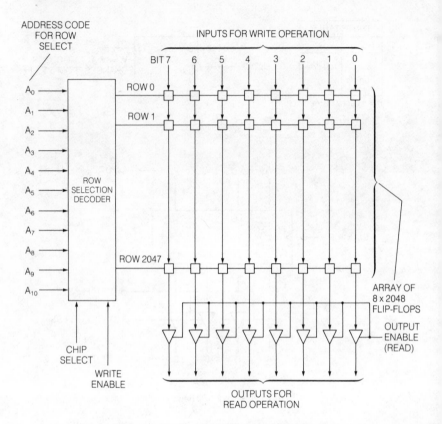

Figure 3-13. *Static RAM Circuit Structure*

In the example of *Figure 3-13*, there are 8 columns or 8-bits per location and 2048 rows or locations. Thus, this memory can store 2048 8-bit codes.

In order for this array to be useful, some method must be used so that each location can be accessed individually. Since 2048 is 2^{11}, an 11-bit binary code will provide 2048 different combinations. This 11-bit code is called an address code or just address. The address code is an input to the memory circuit that specifies which location (from 0 to 2047) is being accessed by the computer. The chip select line is made true by the computer to select this particular memory circuit instead of some other memory circuit. The output enable control works in the same way as the register output enable described in *Figure 3-12*. The output enable is made true by the computer when it wants to read (fetch) what's stored in the memory. The write enable control is made true when the computer wants to write (store) the information on the input lines into a row of the memory.

Unlike the register and D flip-flop of *Figure 3-12*, the static RAM flip-flop is a device that responds to the inputs in a write or storage operation during the time that the write enable signal is true. In other words, there is no clock pulse in the RAM that defines when the storage takes place. The RAM simply requires that the data remain on the inputs while the address inputs are stable and while the write enable signal is true for a sufficient time to insure the storage takes place in the flip-flops without error. However, it should be noted that clock signals are used in the addressing and enabling circuits to ensure correct timing.

The static RAM memory circuit of *Figure 3-13* is only one type of random access memory used in modern digital control systems. Another common type is the dynamic RAM which uses capacitors to store the bit level of a code within the memory. A dynamic RAM can store more bits per circuit than a static RAM. However, a dynamic RAM loses the stored information over a very short period of time (milliseconds) and the information must be refreshed on a periodic basis. A static RAM maintains the stored information as long as electrical operating power is applied to the device. However, both the static and dynamic memory lose all stored information when operating power is removed. Because of this, these types are called volatile memory.

Read-Only Memory

One type of non-volatile memory is called a read-only memory (ROM). This type of memory allows only read operations. The information is stored in the interconnections and logical functions of the memory. Since the bit patterns or codes are fixed once these interconnections are fixed, the memory cannot be written into. The advantage of the ROM is that the digital codes remain stored when electrical power is removed. The program that controls the system behavior is usually stored in ROM memory, so that the system does not lose its control information when it is turned off and it can start operating properly as soon as the system is turned on.

In digital systems involving memory circuits of the types shown in *Figures 3-12* and *3-13*, other types of circuits are needed to provide proper control of the memory circuits. These circuits also are used in digital control systems that do not have a central computer. Three of these circuits are shown in *Figure 3-14*.

Decoders, Encoders, Multiplexers

Decoder

The device shown in *Figure 3-14a* is known as a decoder. It provides an output on one of N lines which is selected by the binary code on one of the n input lines, where $N = 2^n$. Thus, with $n = 3$ as shown, $2^3 = 8$, so there are 8 possible outputs for the 3-bit input code. A 1 will appear on only the one of 8 output lines selected by the input code. For example, if the code 010 is on the inputs, a 1 is on output line 2. This is the type of decoder used in *Figure 3-13* to select 1 of the 2048 rows using an 11-bit input code.

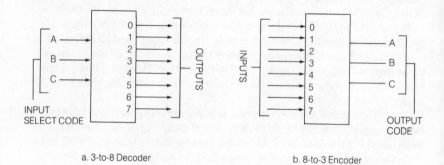

a. 3-to-8 Decoder

b. 8-to-3 Encoder

c. 8-Line-to-One-Line Multiplexer

Figure 3-14. *Digital Selection and Coding Circuits*

Encoder

The device that performs the opposite function is known as an encoder as shown in *Figure 3-14b*. It produces a 3-bit output code that corresponds to the one input line active of 8 line inputs. For example, if an input occurs on line 5, the 3-bit output code is 101. These devices usually have a built-in priority selection, such that if two or more input lines have an active input signal at the same time, only the higher priority line will generate the output code.

Multiplexer

The N-line to 1-line multiplexer shown in *Figure 3-14c* has an n-bit select code with $N = 2^n$. This device acts like a multi-position switch and connects the selected input line to the single output line. The line selected is determined by the 3-bit select code. Thus, the multiplexer shown in *Figure 3-14c* can route one of 8 input signals to the output line.

Many of the digital functions described in this section are used to construct a digital control system either with or without computer control. However, many modern control systems are being constructed using a microcomputer, so the operation of this digital component also must be understood. Let's look at some of the main features of microcomputer architecture and operation.

HOW COMPUTERS ARE USED IN CONTROL SYSTEMS

The computer-based control system has many advantages over a control system that doesn't use a computer. To appreciate the features and advantages of the computer approach, the basic structure and operation of the programmable digital computer must be understood.

A functional block diagram for a typical computer used in a control system is shown in *Figure 3-15*. It shows the relation of the four basic functions—processor, memory, input and output—that are present in any computer system. The processor is the central control function for the system, determining at each point in time what the system components are to do next. It performs this control function under the direction of instructions stored in the system memory. These instructions make up the computer program. The memory also provides storage of system data, function tables, and decision tables. The input function provides for input of system data from sensors and manual controls (such as switches) into the processor. The processor interprets the data and implements output control decisions under the control of the program stored in memory. The output function provides the means for the processor to send the output control signals to the devices that provide system actions.

The processor communicates to the other components in the system using address codes (typically 16-bit codes) on the address bus, and using timing and control signals on the control bus. The address code determines which input, output or memory location is to be activated. The control and timing signals determine which direction data is to flow (to or from the processor) and when the transfer of data is to take place. The actual data codes are sent to or from the processor on the data bus. Data codes are typically 8 or 16 bits long, depending on the type of processor.

Each action the processor takes is under the direction of an instruction from memory. Thus, the processor must determine where the instruction is located in memory and obtain (fetch) that instruction code from memory with a memory read operation. The instruction code is transferred from memory over the data bus to the processor. Once the instruction code is inside the processor, an instruction decoder circuit in the processor determines what the instruction is. Then, a controller within the processor causes the sequence of timing and address code signals to occur in order to execute the instruction. This sequence of address memory, fetch instruction, decode instruction, and execute instruction is repeated for all instructions in the program being executed.

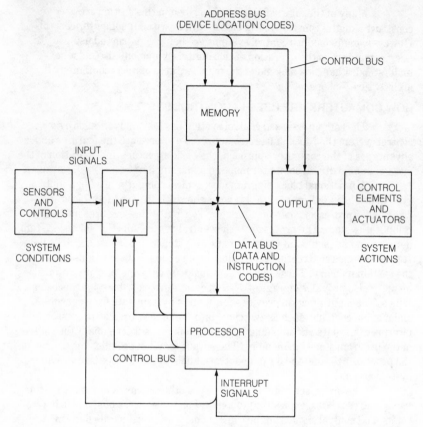

Figure 3-15. *Computer-Based Control System*

Subroutines

Generally, the program in system memory is composed of many short subprograms or subroutines. Each subroutine is devoted to a specific task such as handling some input task, performing some computations or logical data manipulations, or performing some output task. Instructions within a particular subroutine are stored in sequential locations in system memory. Thus, for a subroutine, the processor must access successive memory locations by starting at the first instruction location and adding one to the location code for each successive instruction or next portion of the current instruction. Once a subroutine is finished, the last instruction in the subroutine tells the processor to return to the main program that it was running somewhere else in memory by using a memory address remembered when the subroutine started. Similarly, when an instruction tells the processor to begin execution of a new subroutine that does not begin at the next memory location, the beginning location of the subroutine must be given in the instruction.

The location code is usually held in a particular register in the processor. This register has the capability of counting up by 1 by adding 1 to the value in the register to get the next value or location code. This register is usually called the program counter. It maintains the address of the *next* sequential instruction to be fetched and executed.

Instructions

The instruction types that are available for execution in most processors include data transfer instructions (such as input and output instructions), arithmetic operations (such as addition and subtraction), logical operations (such as AND and OR), comparision instructions (XOR), and program control instructions (such as JUMP to a new location, CALL a subroutine, and RETURN from a subroutine). The JUMP, CALL, and RETURN instructions cause the program counter in the processor to be loaded with a new starting value. The other instructions cause the program counter to increment by one through the sequence of successive instructions.

The operation of the processor and the other system functions can be demonstrated better with an example. *Figures 3-16* through *3-19* show the execution of some instructions that are frequently used in control systems. *Figures 3-16* and *3-17* show the fetching of an input instruction and the execution of that instruction. *Figure 3-18* shows a typical data processing operation using a functional look-up table stored in system memory. *Figure 3-19* shows the execution of an output instruction. This particular sequence of activities is encountered in almost all control actions, since a control system generally monitors input data, examines and manipulates these data in a prescribed manner to determine what action to take, and then generates the output code that causes the needed action.

Fetch

The first part of any instruction cycle performed by the processor is the instruction fetch. A fetch is illustrated in *Figure 3-16* for an INPUT PORT5 instruction. Although this instruction is shown in an English language form, the actual instruction is stored in memory as a specific binary code. It is stored in two consecutive 8-bit locations. The first 8-bit code indicates the INPUT operation and the second 8-bit code indicates the PORT5 address or location code. At the beginning of this example, the program counter contains the address of the first 8-bits of this instruction and the processor puts this address onto the address bus. The controller circuit then enables the memory for a read operation with one or more control signals. The memory places the 8-bit code from the addressed location on the data bus. Another control signal latches (stores) the instruction code into an instruction register in the processor. The decoder decodes the instruction code and determines that it is an INPUT instruction. The processor knows (by design) that it must fetch the next 8-bits to complete an INPUT instruction, so the processor increments (adds one to) the program counter to locate the next portion of the instruction, and again causes a memory read to occur. The code from memory again is placed on the data bus, but this time the code (the PORT5 code) is stored in the second half of the instruction register. This completes the fetching of the INPUT PORT5 instruction. The program counter is incremented to point to the next instruction and the processor begins execution of the INPUT PORT5 instruction.

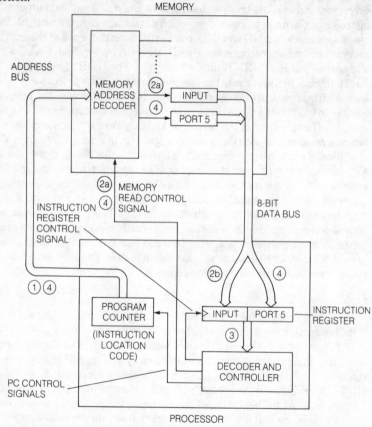

Operations

① Place address of first part of instruction on address bus.

② Perform memory read and store instruction code in instruction register.

③ Interpret instruction and determine if a second read is needed to get next part of address.

④ Perform memory read with next address to get rest of instruction in the instruction register.

Figure 3-16. Instruction Fetch

Execution

The execution phase of the INPUT PORT5 instruction is shown in *Figure 3-17*. In this figure, it is assumed that the input register that responds to the INPUT PORT5 instruction is connected through an amplifier and A/D converter to a temperature sensor. Thus, the 8-bit code in the input register is the binary number that represents the temperature of some portion of the system being controlled. The instruction to be executed (INPUT PORT5) will input this value into a register on the processor called the A register.

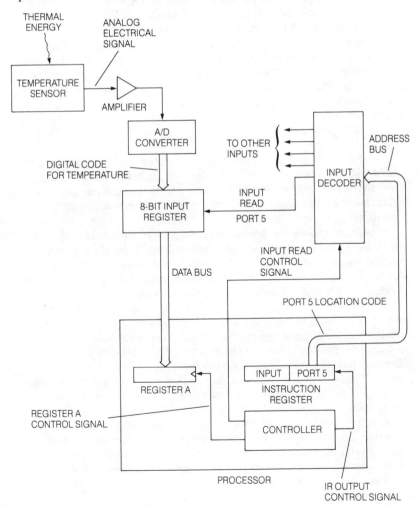

Figure 3-17. *Execution of Input Instruction*

Recall that the PORT5 address code was obtained in the last 8-bits in the fetch operation and stored in the instruction register. Now this PORT5 location code is sent out on the address bus to an input decoder. The input decoder sends an input read signal to the PORT5 input register which holds the temperature code. This enables the output of the register and places the temperature code on the data bus. This is similar to the operation of the memory decoder circuit of *Figure 3-16* that allowed a memory read to output the appropriate memory code onto the data bus. A signal from the controller latches the temperature code into the processor's A register. The input read signal is removed and the execution phase of the INPUT PORT5 instruction is complete. With an INPUT instruction such as this, the command codes entered by a system operator or the digital codes representing the state of the control environment can be input into the processor for eventual storage into system memory or for arithmetic or logical manipulation within the processor. Typically, the total instruction cycle consisting of the fetch and execution operations takes around 3 microseconds for an 8-bit processor (one that uses an 8-bit data bus).

Look-Up Table

An example of one type of input data processing that occurs in most control system applications is shown in *Figure 3-18*. In this case, the output of the control system is governed by a look-up table stored in memory. The "index" to the proper output value in the table is a direct function of the system input.

The processor first places the starting address of the look-up table (shown as 00_{16} in *Figure 3-18*) in an address register. Then, the 8-bit code from the input register that represents the input variable is added to the starting address. The result is the address of the data stored in the look-up table that corresponds to the input condition. The processor then reads the data in that memory location by placing the computed address on the address bus, a memory read timing signal on the control bus, and stores the resulting code from the data bus in the A register for further processing.

The table in *Figure 3-18* can hold 256 ($FF_{16} + 1$) entries. Thus, 256 different input codes can be correlated to 256 output codes.

The table may represent a function that must be implemented. For example, if a temperature sensor output signal is not linear; that is, the digital code value is not proportional to temperature, correction values could be stored in the table to correct for the non-linearity and produce a set of 8-bit codes that precisely represent the temperature in a proportional manner. Alternatively, the table values could represent a blower motor speed so that for different temperatures measured by the sensor, a different blower motor speed would be selected from the table to provide optimum air delivery in a heating system.

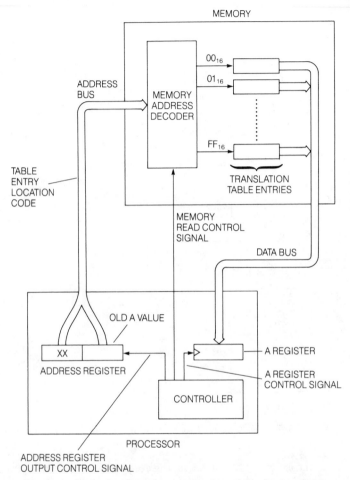

Figure 3-18. *Execution of a Table Look-Up Instruction*

Output Control

Now that the output control digital code is in the A register, the processor can send the value to the appropriate output device by executing an output instruction like the OUTPUT PORT3 instruction illustrated in *Figure 3-19*. The instruction code is fetched as previously discussed so the instruction code and the location code for PORT3 are in the processor register. Then, the processor outputs the PORT3 location code on the address bus and provides register output timing signals to the output decoder. The output decoder sends a latch signal to the appropriate output register so that the data coming out of the processor from the A register on the data bus will be stored in that output register. The external circuit will then provide the desired output action.

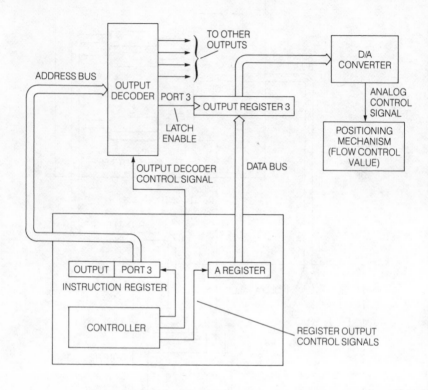

Figure 3-19. *Execution of an Output Instruction*

In the example of *Figure 3-19*, the desired action is the adjustment of a flow control valve. The digital output code is converted to an analog equivalent signal by the D/A converter. The analog signal drives a mechanism which adjusts the position of a flow control valve in a hot water heating system. The valve is opened or closed depending on the temperature sensed in the input operation of *Figure 3-16*.

Some outputs may be only single digital bits to control the on or off state of a device such as a motor or relay. Such a bit can be one of the eight bits of one of the output registers or it can be an individual flip-flop that responds to one of the OUTPUT instructions.

Interrupts

The interrupt signals shown in *Figure 3-15* may be generated by some of the input or output circuits to get the attention of the processor. (An interrupt could be compared to a student in class raising his/her hand to get the attention of the teacher.) The processor responds to the signal by performing a jump to a subroutine that is designed to handle the input or output condition that caused the interrupt signal. The importance of the interrupt signaling capability is that it allows the processor to handle its other tasks without the time-consuming job of continually monitoring the input and output circuits. (To continue the classroom analogy, continual monitoring would be like the teacher asking each student individually in turn if he/she has a question or comment.) When these circuits need service, they can get the processor's attention by using the interrupt signal. The processor spends only the time necessary to handle the actual input or output need.

Advantages of Using a Computer

Using a computer in control system design has several advantages that now can be appreciated. In the first place, one computer functions much like any other computer. Computer functions can be purchased in individual circuit form or an entire microcomputer can be purchased as a single integrated circuit. The result is that very little hardware design is required to produce a system, and very little redesign is required to change the system operation.

The other and equally important advantage is that the system behavior is governed by the program stored in the system memory. To change the actions of the control system, the program simply is changed, usually by replacing an integrated circuit ROM in the system. Thus, the computer approach is very versatile and easily adaptable to any application. Also, it can be configured to act as a non-computer digital system or an analog system. One simply has to select the control structure and strategy for a given application, then provide the appropriate input and output circuits and application program. Some of these alternatives will be considered next.

GENERAL FEATURES OF ELECTRONIC CONTROL SYSTEMS

The structure of a computer-based control system is much like that shown in *Figure 3-15*. A general form that would be applicable to non-computer based and digital control systems is shown in *Figure 3-20*.

Sensors convert environmental variables and system state variables into equivalent electrical signals that are applied to the input circuits. Other input circuits monitor operator control settings, such as switch positions or variable resistor settings. These operator commands are usually already in electrical signal form.

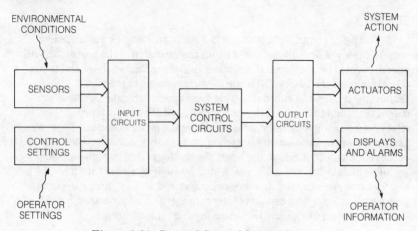

Figure 3-20. General Control System Structure

The input circuits amplify these electrical signals and pass them into the system control circuits. These control circuits process the input information and determine the appropriate actions to be taken. The signals required to produce these actions are sent to the output circuits. The analog output circuits provide the proper voltage and current level and waveshape to actuators and/or display and alarm devices. Actuators are devices such as solenoid valves that perform an action. Displays provide ON-OFF indications or alphanumeric information about system status. Audible and/or visual alarms alert the operator to a system malfunction or dangerous condition.

Open-Loop Systems

A control system can be configured for open-loop or closed-loop control. In an open-loop system, the control circuits do not monitor the system output to determine if the desired control function was achieved. In a closed-loop system, a feedback sensor and circuit does monitor the controlled function. The feedback circuit develops a correction signal that is applied to the control circuits to adjust the output toward the desired value. In an open-loop system, the control circuits determine the signals to send to the actuator elements that should, by plan and design, cause the system to achieve the operational status required by the control setting.

The time response of an open-loop system typically is as shown in *Figure 3-21a*. The system starts out with a controlled variable such as speed or temperature at one value with the control settings requiring the system to go to a new value. The functional characteristic of the control circuits will cause the controlled variable to change to a value near the specified new value. There may be an error in this final value; that is, the actual value may not quite equal the desired value because of system errors. Further, the response may be relatively slow to ensure a predictable response to the control setting command.

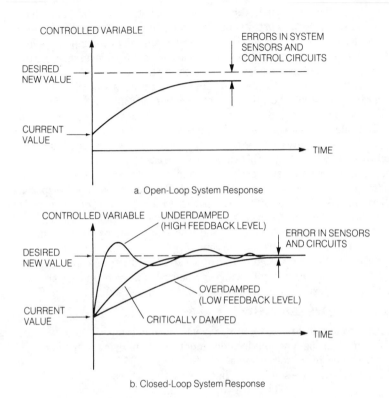

a. Open-Loop System Response

b. Closed-Loop System Response

Figure 3-21. *Typical Control System Response Characteristics*

Closed-Loop System

In a closed-loop system, sensors continually monitor the current value of the controlled variable. Thus, if a desired temperature is set at the input of a heating system and the actual temperature is monitored by a sensor, the desired versus actual temperature values are continually compared and system action taken to make the two values approach equal. There may still be a final error in the actual temperature due to errors in the sensor measurement of the temperature, but the error should be much smaller than that in a comparable open-loop system.

The response of the closed-loop system can be adjusted. Various response times and the system action is shown in *Figure 3-21b*. The response depends on how much weight is placed on the sensed value by the amplification circuits connected to the feedback sensor. If the feedback amplification is low and the control circuits primarily respond to the input control settings, the situation is similar to the open-loop system and the time response is similar. This is called an overdamped response.

On the other hand, if the amplification in the sensor signal path is so high that small changes in the controlled variable causes large changes in the feedback signal to the control circuits, the system will overcompensate in its correction. It will first drive the control variable too high (overshooting the desired value) and then too low (undershooting the desired value) before finally settling down to the desired value. Such a response is called underdamped. It has the advantage of bringing the controlled variable to the desired value very fast, but the oscillations (variations) above and below the desired value are not wanted. In fact, if the feedback amplification is set too high, the system never settles down to the desired value and continually oscillates above and below this value. In some cases, the system can become self-destructive under such oscillatory conditions. Intermediate between the underdamped and overdamped responses is the critically damped response where the feedback amplification is such that it brings the controlled variable to the desired level as fast as possible without overshooting the value.

Both the open-loop and closed-loop configurations are used and various response times are used in control system design in both analog and digital control systems. Some of the applications of digital and analog signals and various control strategies will be presented in the remaining chapters of this book as specific energy control systems are discussed.

WHAT HAVE WE LEARNED?

1. Analog electrical signals continually vary in amplitude.
2. Common analog functions include amplification, filtering, summing, integration and differentiation.
3. Digital signals are signals that have two states represented by two levels of voltage or current. The two levels represent a 1 or 0 state.
4. The data or information is contained in the voltage levels of digital circuits.
5. Transition times are important to the synchronization of digital circuits and systems.
6. Common digital functions include logical operations (OR, AND, XOR, and NOT), storage functions, decoding, encoding and multiplexing.
7. Circuits are available that convert signals from analog to digital or digital to analog. These are commonly called A/D and D/A converters.
8. Digital computers consist of the processor, memory, input, and output functions.
9. Control systems may be open-loop or closed-loop, depending on whether or not the controlled variable is monitored and compared to the desired value.

Quiz for Chapter 3

1. A sinusoidal signal has a frequency of 1,000 hertz. What is the period of this signal in milliseconds (thousandths of a second)?
   a. 0.1
   b. 1
   c. 100
   d. 1,000

2. A sinusoidal voltage signal has a peak value of 100 volts. Its rms value is approximately:
   a. 50
   b. 60
   c. 70
   d. 80

3. In a circuit of the type shown in Figure 3-5a with $R1 = 0.1R2$, and $V_1 = 2$ and $V_2 = 1.5$, what is the value of V_o in volts?
   a. -1
   b. -5
   c. 1
   d. 5
   e. 10

4. If a low-pass filter with a cut-off frequency of 1,000 hertz is in series with a high-pass filter with a cut-off frequency of 1,100 hertz, the result is a:
   a. low pass filter with a cut-off frequency of 1,100 hertz.
   b. high pass filter with a cut-off frequency of 1,000 hertz.
   c. bandpass filter with a bandwidth of 100 hertz.
   d. band reject filter that rejects frequencies between 1,000 and 1,100 hertz.

5. A digital binary code of 10110011 is represented in hexadecimal number form as:
   a. 10110011
   b. 2303
   c. B3
   d. 179

6. The decimal equivalent of the binary number code of problem 5 is:
   a. B3
   b. 127
   c. 176
   d. 179

7. If a telephone signal contains 4,000 hertz as its highest frequency sinusoid, how often (in samples per second) would this signal have to be sampled to avoid loss of information?
   a. 1,000
   b. 2,000
   c. 4,000
   d. 6,000
   e. 8,000

8. A hexadecimal number 2A4F has the decimal equivalent of:
   a. 4,098
   b. 6,123
   c. 10,533
   d. 10,831
   e. 12,543

9. The output of an exclusive-OR gate will be 0 if:
   a. both inputs are zero.
   b. both inputs are one.
   c. the inputs are opposite (a 0 and a 1 or vice-versa).
   d. a and b above.

10. A RAM that has a 14-bit address input can contain how many storage locations?
    a. 2,048
    b. 4,096
    c. 8,192
    d. 16,384
    e. 17,000

11. A decoder is a device that:
    a. outputs a logical 1 on one of 2^n lines selected by an n-bit code.
    b. inputs a signal from one of 2^n lines selected by an n-bit code.
    c. provides an n-bit code that corresponds to which of 2^n input lines has a logical 1.

12. A multiplexer is a device that:
    a. outputs a logical 1 on one of 2^n lines selected by an n-bit code.
    b. inputs a signal from one of 2^n lines selected by an n-bit code.
    c. provides an n-bit code that corresponds to which of 2^n input lines has a logical 1.

13. How many memory references (reads) are required to fetch the instruction of Figure 3-16?
    a. none
    b. 1
    c. 2
    d. 3

14. An open-loop control system differs from a closed-loop control system in that:
    a. the output is a function only of the inputs in an open-loop system while the output is a function of both the inputs and the present output in a closed-loop system.
    b. the output of a closed-loop system is a function of the present output level only.
    c. the output of an open-loop system is a function of the present output level only.
    d. the output of a closed-loop system is only a function of the inputs.

15. A high feedback level may result in a response known as:
    a. underdamped.
    b. critically damped.
    c. overdamped.
    d. oscillatory.
    e. none of the above.
    f. a and d above.

16. When compared with an overdamped response, an underdamped response causes the system to reach the desired output level at a rate that is:
    a. faster.
    b. slower.
    c. same rate.

17. A critically damped control system:
    a. reaches the desired output value faster than an underdamped system.
    b. reaches the desired output level faster than an overdamped system.
    c. causes oscillation above and below the desired output value.
    d. does not reliably reach the output level desired.

18. The purpose of the address in a computer is to:
    a. provide information to the instruction.
    b. determine the location in the system of a digital code.
    c. provide a control code to the processor controller.
    d. provide a numerical code for output devices.

19. The purpose of the program counter in a processor is to:
    a. provide the address of a data code.
    b. count the number of instructions that have been executed.
    c. provide the address of an instruction code.
    d. provide the instruction code that is to be executed next.

20. The advantage of using a microcomputer controller over a non-microcomputer controller is:
    a. low-cost realization of complex systems.
    b. simple design and redesign of the control system.
    c. versatile and adaptable design structures.
    d. all of the above.
    e. none of the above.

How to Control Motors and Generators

ABOUT THIS CHAPTER

In Chapter 2, the principles of the electromechanical generator for converting mechanical energy to electrical energy were discussed. You may want to review that discussion before reading this chapter. This chapter relates the generator action to motor action, then electronic control of electric motors is discussed. The chapter concludes with a discussion about the electronic control of electric power generation and transmission by utility companies.

ELECTRIC MOTOR PRINCIPLES

If a conductor has current flowing through it, a magnetic field surrounds that conductor. This is shown in *Figure 4-1a.* The greater the current, the stronger the magnetic field. The direction of the field is determined by the right hand rule as shown in *Figure 4-1b.* Let's apply this principle to explain motor action—converting electrical energy into mechanical energy.

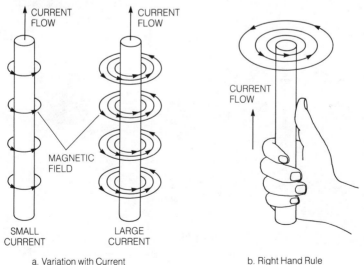

a. Variation with Current   b. Right Hand Rule

Figure 4-1. *Magnetic Field Around Current Carrying Conductors*

Motor Action

A current-carrying conductor that is free to move is placed in a stationary magnetic field as shown in *Figure 4-2a*. The magnetic field that surrounds the conductor due to the current flow interacts with the stationary magnetic field to apply a force on the conductor to make it move. This is shown in *Figure 4-2b*. The current flow is into the wire; therefore, the magnetic field produced by the current is clockwise around the conductor. The stationary field is from right to left. Below the conductor, a stronger magnetic field is produced because the two fields aid each other. Above the conductor, a weaker magnetic field is produced because the two fields oppose each other. With a strong field on the bottom and a weak field on the top, the magnetic force pushes the conductor up and converts electrical energy to mechanical energy. The force moving the conductor is applied in a direction that is at a right angle to the direction of the field and at a right angle to the direction of the current flow.

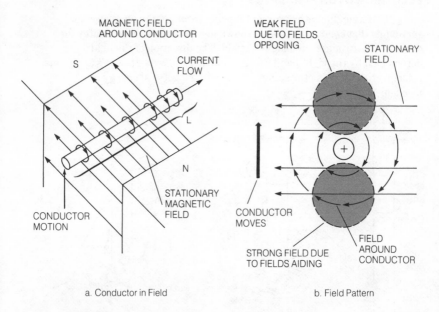

a. Conductor in Field   b. Field Pattern

Figure 4-2. *Motor Action*

In *Figure 4-3*, the conductor is formed into a coil. In *Figure 4-3a*, the conventional current flows into the paper on the left side of the coil and out of the paper on the right side of the coil. With the coil positioned as it is, and with the magnetic field lines from the field magnet going from right to left (N to S), the force on the left side of the coil is upward and the force on the right side of the coil is downward. These forces cause the coil to rotate in a clockwise direction if the coil is fastened at each end along its axis in such a way that only rotation is allowed. In *Figure 4-3b*, the coil is rotated 180° from the position of *Figure 4-3a*. Now the current in the left side of the coil flows out of the paper and the current in the right side of the coil flows into the paper. The forces on the coil are reversed from *Figure 4-3a* and cause the coil to rotate in a counter-clockwise direction. If the coil is first in the position of *Figure 4-3a* and rotates clockwise past the vertical position to the position of *Figure 4-3b*, the direction of rotation will reverse. This back and forth motion of the coil around the vertical position will continue until the coil finally comes to rest at a vertical position as shown in *Figure 4-3c*.

In this case, the top part of the coil has current flow into the paper with a force away from the coil axis, and the bottom part of the coil has current flow out of the paper with a force also away from the coil axis. Thus, no force is exerted on the coil to make it move either clockwise or counter-clockwise and the coil remains stationary in a vertical position. Therefore, a coil with a constant current flowing through it in the same direction at all times in a constant stationary magnetic field will eventually stop rotating and come to a rest at either the vertical position shown in *Figure 4-3c* or the vertical position 180° from it. This type of device is not capable of producing continuous rotation for a steady rotating mechanical energy output. Some means must be provided for either reversing the magnetic field lines as the coil passes through the vertical plane, or some means must be provided for reversing the coil current as it passes through the vertical plane. The first method is used in ac motors and the second method is used in dc motors.

Commutator

For dc motors, the current reversal is achieved through the use of a commutator on the coil axis. (You may want to review the commutator action as discussed in Chapter 2 for the generator.) The commutator switching changes the current direction and keeps the coil rotating in the same direction to provide continual rotational mechanical energy output.

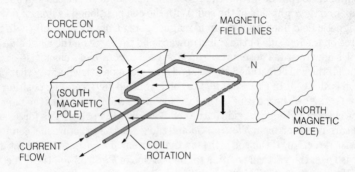

a. Clockwise Rotation

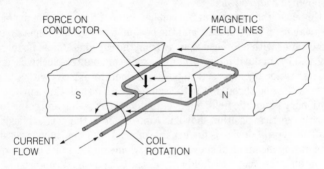

b. Counter-Clockwise Rotation

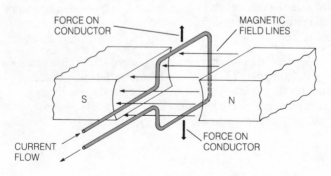

c. No Rotation

***Figure 4-3.** Forces on a Coil of Wire with Constant Current in a Constant Stationary, Magnetic Field*

Producing the Stationary Magnetic Fields

The magnetic poles of the motor, indicated by the permanent magnets of *Figure 4-2*, can be produced by passing current through coils of wire wound around soft iron cores as shown in *Figure 4-4*. These windings are referred to as the field windings because they produce the stationary magnetic field which reacts with the field generated by the armature coil current to provide the force to turn the motor shaft. Small dc motors may use permanent magnets for magnetic poles to produce the magnetic field, but large motors use field windings to produce the magnetic poles. The soft iron core of the windings provides an easy flow path for the magnetic field lines and helps to concentrate the field and keep it uniform in the area of the poles.

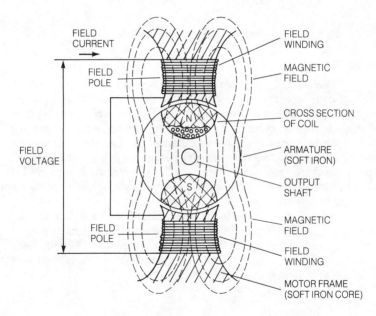

Figure 4-4. *Magnetic Poles from Field Windings*

Summary of Motor Action

Figure 4-5 is a simplified schematic diagram of a motor. To set the motor action firmly in mind, let's summarize what happens using this schematic. A voltage is applied to the field winding. Current flows in the winding as a result of the voltage, forming the magnetic poles and uniform stationary magnetic field inside the motor housing. Current flows in the armature as a result of a voltage applied to the armature windings (coils) and produces another magnetic field. The interaction of the magnetic fields produces the force that turns the armature and the output shaft of the motor.

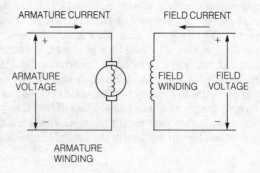

Figure 4-5. *Schematic of Motor*

Counter EMF

The electrical resistance of the armature winding is very small; therefore, large amounts of current would flow continually in the windings when a voltage is applied if it were not for an electrical force called "counter emf". Counter emf is produced in the armature winding because a rotating armature winding acts like a generator. Remember that generator action is produced when conductors move through a magnetic field. That is exactly what the armature windings are doing. As the windings are being forced around by the motor action, generator action takes place and the counter emf is developed in the armature winding.

Counter emf is shown in the schematic of *Figure 4-6*. It is a voltage that is in series with the armature winding and of a polarity such that it opposes V_A, the voltage applied to the armature winding. As a result, the armature current is much smaller and is regulated by the counter emf because the counter emf opposes the applied voltage.

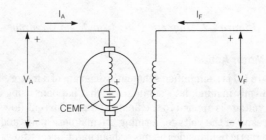

Figure 4-6. *Counter EMF*

The counter emf voltage is a real advantage. It tends to regulate motor speed since it is proportional to speed. If a motor slows down, the counter emf is less. This allows more armature current to flow which speeds up the motor. The reverse is true if a motor speeds up.

AC POWER

Single-Phase Power

In *Figure 4-7a*, the single-phase ac voltage that is normally available at an outlet in a home, office or factory is plotted against time. It is a 60-hertz, 120 volt ac waveform. Since 60 cycles occur in one second, one cycle takes 1/60th of a second or 0.01667 seconds. Engineers, scientists and technicians express this in exponential form as 16.67×10^{-3} seconds, and convert the 10^{-3} to a word form abbreviation of "milli". Therefore, the time of one cycle is 16.67 milliseconds and the time of one-half cycle is 8.33 milliseconds.

If the value of the voltage is stated as 120 VAC, it implies that it is the RMS (root-mean-square) value of the voltage. The RMS value is an ac value that dissipates the same amount of power in a resistor as a constant dc voltage of the same value even though the ac voltage is constantly changing amplitude and reversing direction. Recall that the peak value is given by:

$$\text{Peak Value} = 1.414 \times \text{RMS Value}$$

Therefore, a 120 VAC sine wave has a peak value of $1.414 \times 120 = 169.7$ volts peak.

Three-Phase Power

Power delivered by the electric power company to industrial plants for large motors and heavy industrial equipment is three-phase power (abbreviated 3φ). A 3φ power waveform is shown in *Figure 4-7b*. The three voltages are separated in time by 120° of electrical rotation because three separate coils physically placed 120° apart are wound on the generator armature.

AC MOTORS

There are two general types of ac motors—synchronous and induction motors. For applications less than 5 to 10 horsepower, either dc motors or single-phase ac induction motors are used. For higher power applications for heavy industrial use, ac three-phase induction or synchronous motors are used. Three-phase motors use a rotating magnetic field to produce motor action. Let's see how a rotating magnetic field is produced.

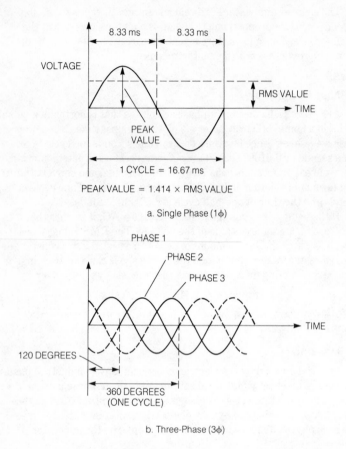

a. Single Phase (1φ)

b. Three-Phase (3φ)

Figure 4-7. 60 Hz AC Power

Rotating Magnetic Field

Three pairs of pole pieces with field coil windings are positioned around an armature in *Figure 4-8a*; one pair for each phase of a 3φ ac motor. Each pair has the voltage of one of the phases of a 3φ power system applied to it. At time period t_1, when the sine wave of phase 1 is at its positive peak, the phase 1 pair produces a north pole at the top of the armature and a south pole at the bottom. Time t_2 is 120 electrical degrees later and is the time when the phase 2 voltage is at its positive peak. Therefore, a north pole is produced at the top of the armature and a south pole at the bottom. Time t_3 is 120 electrical degrees later in time and is the time when the phase 3 voltage is at its positive peak. A north pole is produced at the top of the armature and a south pole at the bottom. The three phase voltages have the time relationship shown in *Figure 4-7b*.

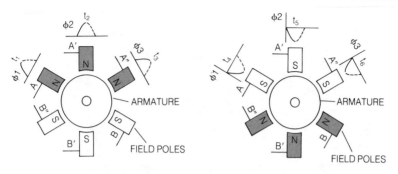

a. Positive Alternation of Phases   b. Negative Alternation of Phases

Figure 4-8. *Rotating Magnetic Field*

Times t_4, t_5 and t_6 of *Figure 4-8b* are also points in time separated by 120 electrical degrees of the 60-hertz sine wave applied to the field windings. The phase voltages reach their negative peaks at these times in the sequence indicated by *Figure 4-7b*. As the voltages reach their negative peaks, the magnetic fields are at a maximum, but in the opposite direction from what they were in *Figure 4-8a*. Now the north pole is on the bottom of the armature and the south pole is on the top. The north pole is still moving clockwise and the magnetic field is expanding and contracting as the voltage increases and decreases.

It should be apparent from this discussion and from *Figure 4-8*, that as time progresses from t_1 to t_6, the magnetic field produced by the three phases is rotating clockwise around the armature. It should also be apparent that if current is flowing in a coil in the armature, the moving magnetic field and the motor action previously discussed will cause the armature to turn as the magnetic field rotates. This is the basic principle used for the field in an ac motor.

Synchronous Motor

In the synchronous motor, the armature coil current always flows in the same direction because a commutator is used. Thus, the armature coil acts like a bar magnet within a rotating magnetic field as shown in *Figure 4-9*. The rotating magnetic field pulls the armature "bar magnet" along with it to produce a mechanical motion that is revolving at the same (or almost the same) speed as the electrically rotated magnetic field. The armature lags slightly behind the rotating magnetic field. As the mechanical load on the motor output shaft increases, the armature magnet falls further behind the rotating magnetic field. This produces more torque (more mechanical energy), but at a slightly lower speed. Because of the nature of the synchronous motor action, the speed is fixed by the structure of the motor and there is no practical way to control the motor speed.

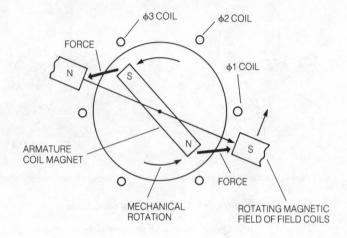

Figure 4-9. Synchronous AC Motor Action

Induction Motor

The motor action in the induction motor is very similar to the synchronous motor; however, the construction of the armature is different. In fact, the armature is called a rotor in this motor. The rotor windings are just closed coils of wire with no external connections; thus, there is no externally applied voltage to the rotor. Its operation depends on the basic principle that a changing magnetic field cutting across a conductor induces a current in the conductor. The changing magnetic field produced by the field windings induces a circulating current in the rotor coil loops; thus, the name induction motor. The circulating current in the closed coils develops its own magnetic field in the rotor and the interaction between the rotor field and the field of the field coils is what causes the motor action.

This action is shown in *Figure 4-10* with the direction of magnetic field produced by the field coils, the rotor current direction, and the resultant force and direction of rotation indicated. Both the positive and negative alternation of the ac voltage are shown. Note that the field reverses direction just at the right time to keep the force in the same direction and the rotor turning in a clockwise direction.

The rotor rotates once for each cycle of the field current. If 60-hertz ac power is applied, the motor of *Figure 4-10* will rotate at 60 revolutions per second or 3600 revolutions per minute. As the mechanical load increases, the rotor speed decreases. The relationship between the torque and the rotor speed for an induction motor is shown in *Figure 4-11*. The maximum speed corresponds to a no-load situation and is determined by the frequency of the applied voltage, the magnitude of the applied voltage, the rotor current, and the number of field poles in the structure.

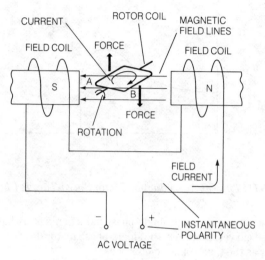

a. Positive Alternation

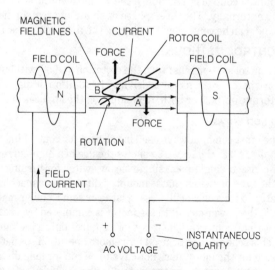

b. Negative Alternation

Figure 4-10. *Operation of AC Induction Motor*

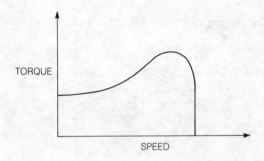

Figure 4-11. *Typical AC Induction Motor Speed-Torque Characteristics*

The three-phase and single-phase induction motors have similar torque-speed curves; however, the single-phase motor does not need a commutator as the three-phase motor does.

The three-phase synchronous motor has speed-torque curves similar to those of the induction motor, but there is little control over its speed. A limited amount of control is available if the wound armature coils can be connected to externally. The three-phase or single-phase induction motors, on the other hand, can be controlled by varying the field voltage or frequency.

MOTOR CONTROL METHODS

A control system must turn the motor on and off without damaging the motor or whatever the motor is driving. In addition, it may control the speed, the torque output, or both, depending on the application.

Older Common Ways

The most common ways used in the past for controlling motors are shown in *Figure 4-12*. *Figure 4-12a* shows the use of a high-current, mechanical-contact, single-pole, single-throw switch for turning the motor on or off. It's the type of switch that is mounted directly on a machine and is used by an operator to turn on a drill press, a lathe or some similar machine. In *Figure 4-12b*, the power circuit to the motor is completed by a set of high-current relay contacts. The relay coil requires only a low current for operation. This scheme may be used for remote operation so that the high current wiring for the motor does not have to be run for long distances between the control switch and the motor. It also provides safety isolation for the operator since control relays such as this normally are operated from a 24-volt ac power source. For example, the switch in the relay control circuit might be a thermostat in a heating/air conditioning system or a switch on an assembly line.

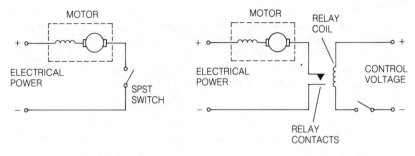

a. Direct Switch Control

b. Relay Control

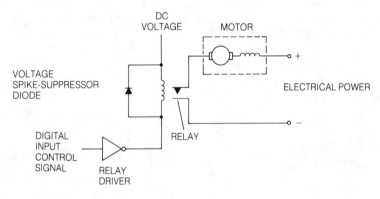

c. Electronic Control

Figure 4-12. *Basic Motor Controls*

Electronic control started with circuits similar to the one shown in *Figure 4-12c.* Here the relay coil current is provided through a solid-state circuit called a relay driver. The input to the driver is usually a digital signal so that an ON or logical 1 signal is in the range of 2.4 to 5 volts and an OFF or logical 0 signal is in the range of 0 to 0.8 volts. The driver shown in *Figure 4-12c* performs logical inversion of the input control signal so that a 1 input produces a 0 output and vice versa. When an ON or 1 signal is input, current flows through the driver output circuit and through the relay coil to energize the relay and close its contacts. When an OFF or 0 signal is input, the output circuit of the driver acts like an open switch. Relay coil current cannot flow; therefore, the relay contacts are open.

A relay coil has inductance that stores a charge when the relay is energized. When the relay coil is de-energized, the stored charge induces a high voltage pulse across the coil. This voltage pulse can damage the relay driver, so a voltage spike-suppressor diode is usually used across the relay coil as shown in *Figure 4-12c.*

Newer Electronic Ways

True and total electronic control of high-current, high-voltage motors began when semiconductor manufacturers started supplying a solid-state device called a Silicon Controlled Rectifier (SCR). The SCR is an electrically-controlled, high-current switch that can directly replace relay contacts or mechanical switch contacts. Let's look at how an SCR operates.

SCR

Figure 4-13a shows an SCR connected to control an ac motor. The SCR takes the place of the relay contacts of *Figure 4-12c*. The SCR has three connections; an anode, a cathode and a gate. The SCR is a device that conducts current only in one direction (unidirectional). It conducts current when the anode is more positive than the cathode and it has been triggered (turned on) by a voltage on the gate that is positive with respect to the cathode. This condition (SCR ON) is shown in *Figure 4-13b*. If these conditions are not met, the device acts as an open circuit and blocks the flow of current. This condition (SCR OFF) is shown in *Figure 4-13c*. This operation is detailed further in *Figure 4-14*.

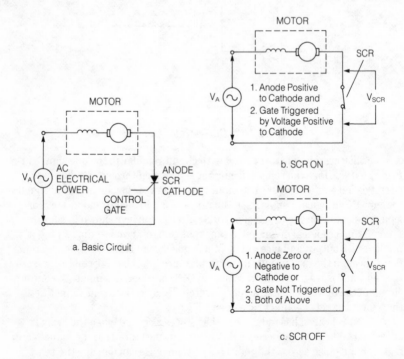

Figure 4-13. Electronic Control of AC Motor

As the input applied voltage of *Figure 4-14a* goes positive to make the SCR anode positive with respect to the cathode, the SCR does not conduct because a voltage has not been applied to the gate to cause gate current to flow. Therefore, the SCR is a high resistance and the applied circuit voltage appears across the SCR as shown in *Figure 4-14d*. At time t_1, a voltage pulse (usually its duration must be a minimum of 20 microseconds) is applied to the gate to cause a current above the rated latching current to flow. The SCR is turned ON and becomes a very low resistance so that full load current flows in the circuit as shown in *Figure 4-14c*. If the gate pulse occurred at time t_0

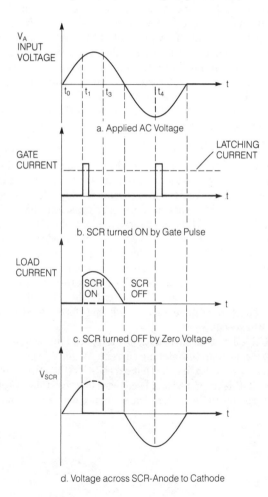

Figure 4-14. *Detailed SCR Operation*

rather than at t_1, the SCR would be turned on sooner and the full load current would flow for the full positive half-cycle of the applied voltage. However, with the SCR triggered at t_1, load current flows only for part of the positive half-cycle. As shown in *Figure 4-14c*, if the SCR were not triggered until t_3, then the load current would flow for only a very small portion of the positive half-cycle. The average power delivered to the load would be quite low compared to the power delivered if the SCR is triggered at t_0. This is how control of the power is accomplished with electronics.

When the applied voltage of *Figure 4-14a* reaches zero and then goes into the negative alternation, the anode voltage of the SCR drops to zero and then goes negative with respect to the cathode. A certain minimum current, called the holding current, must flow in the SCR to maintain its low ON resistance after it is triggered. When the applied voltage approaches zero after the SCR is turned ON, this holding current is no longer maintained and the SCR turns OFF. It becomes a high resistance, no load current flows (*Figure 4-14c*), and the applied voltage appears across the SCR (*Figure 4-14d*). No further load current flows until the SCR anode is positive and is triggered again with sufficient gate current.

An Example SCR Control Circuit

A basic control circuit for a series DC motor or an ac single-phase induction motor based on a resistance-capacitance (RC) time constant is shown in *Figure 4-15*. An SCR controls the load current through the motor. Its trigger time is controlled by a variable resistor, a capacitor and a solid-state device called a DIAC. A DIAC is like a zener diode. It must have a certain voltage across it before it conducts. However, a zener diode needs a voltage of only one polarity, but a DIAC conducts for either polarity. As a result, it is an important device to produce a set voltage drop in ac circuits. Essentially, it acts as a constant voltage, V_1, in series with the gate terminal of the SCR to establish a trigger threshold voltage for the SCR. The DIAC does not conduct current until the constant voltage is exceeded; therefore, the SCR cannot be triggered until V_c exceeds V_1.

The SCR will not turn ON until it is triggered by a current I_{tr}, shown in *Figure 4-15a*, larger than the latching current. When V_c, the voltage across the capacitor, reaches a voltage level that exceeds V_1 (the DIAC voltage) and provides I_{tr}, the SCR is triggered and becomes a low resistance to allow I_L, the load current, to flow in the motor. The sequence of events is shown in *Figure 4-15b*.

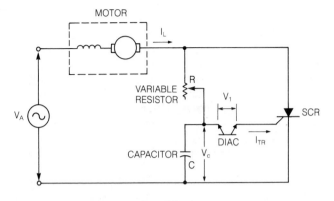

a. Control Circuit

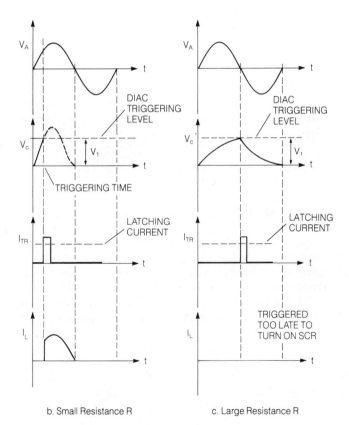

b. Small Resistance R

c. Large Resistance R

Figure 4-15. RC Motor Control

The voltage across the capacitor, V_c, increases as determined by the RC time constant of the variable, R, resistance and the capacitance of C in the charging circuit. The RC time constant is the product of the resistance (in ohms) times the capacitance (in farads). In this circuit, the value of the capacitance is fixed, so the RC time constant is varied by adjusting the variable resistor to change the value of the resistance. If the resistance is small, the capacitor is charged quickly and V_c quickly becomes large enough to trigger the SCR. If the resistance is large, it takes a much longer time for the capacitor to charge enough for V_c to reach the triggering level.

In *Figure 4-15b*, the resistance is small, the rise of V_c is rapid, and the SCR turns ON very near the beginning of the positive alternation of the applied voltage.

In *Figure 4-15c*, the resistance is large, the rise of V_c is slow, and the SCR is never triggered because the voltage across the SCR is so close to zero when the gate current flows that the holding current cannot be maintained.

The motor speed and torque can be controlled by varying the amount of load current, I_L, between the limits of *Figure 4-15b* and *4-15c*. The current pulses occurring in each half-cycle are smoothed out by the motor to represent an average value of current. As a result, the motor speed is controlled by varying the variable resistor of *Figure 4-15a* either manually or electronically.

Another application for this type of circuit is as a light dimmer for electric light control. The light bulb or bulbs would take the place of the motor in *Figure 4-15a*. The variable resistor would be manually adjusted to control light intensity.

TRIAC

Another solid-state device used for control of high-voltage, high-current loads is the TRIAC. It is a sister device to the SCR and, as indicated by its symbol shown in *Figure 4-16a*, acts like two SCRs connected in inverse-parallel (back-to-back). The anode of one SCR is connected to the cathode of the other. As a result, a TRIAC can conduct in either direction and it can be triggered by a positive or negative gate voltage. Therefore, with a TRIAC, load current can flow during both half-cycles of the applied ac voltage rather than just one, as for the SCR. This is shown in *Figure 4-16b* where the gate is triggered at the zero crossover point. Using a TRIAC in the circuit of *Figure 4-15* would allow load current, I_L, to flow during both half-cycles which improves the smoothness of the control and increases the power delivered to the load.

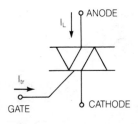

a. Symbol

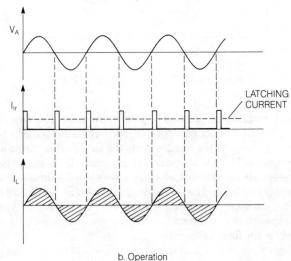

b. Operation

Figure 4-16. *TRIAC*

Thermistor Controlled Motor

A variation of the circuit of *Figure 4-15* is shown in *Figure 4-17*. The control device is a TRIAC and the manually adjustable variable resistor is replaced with a thermistor. A thermistor is a device whose resistance decreases with increasing temperature. Thus, if the thermistor is sensing a cool temperature so that the resistance is very large, very little current is delivered to the motor and the motor is off. As the thermistor temperature increases and thermistor resistance decreases, the TRIAC is turned on earlier in the cycle. The motor current increases and the motor speed increases.

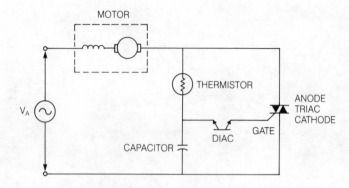

Figure 4-17. Thermistor Motor Control

Such control could be used to provide the needed air flow in a furnace. When the air is cold (furnace off or just turned on), no air would be blown through the air ducts. As the furnace heats the air, the thermistor would allow the blower motor to begin at a slow speed and gradually increase the speed to maximum as the air becomes hotter. Similarly, when the furnace is turned off, the motor continues to run at ever decreasing speeds as the air cools. This would extract the maximum amount of heat from the furnace without delivering any cool air to the rooms. Such a control could significantly increase the efficiency of the furnace operation.

Controls similar to that shown in *Figure 4-15* and *4-17* can provide convenient manual or automatic electronic control of the motor speed of induction and DC motors. If a three-phase motor is to be controlled, a TRIAC would be placed in each rotor winding and triggered by a common control DIAC or by identical control circuits.

DIGITAL CONTROL

All of the control methods presented so far have been based on analog (continually varying) voltages and currents. For digital control, techniques must be used to provide motor control circuits that give similar results by responding to the binary codes of a digital system. If a TRIAC is used as the load control device, there must be a way to control the triggering time of the TRIAC with a digital code. A method using an 8-bit binary control code is shown in *Figure 4-18*. Recall that an 8-bit number has a hexadecimal (base 16) equivalent range from 00 to FF. The corresponding decimal (base 10) equivalent range is from 0 to 255. In other words, whatever is being controlled can be controlled to one part in 256.

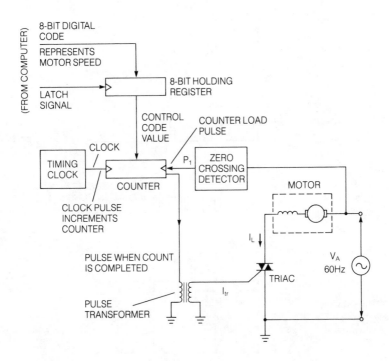

Figure 4-18. *Digital Control of TRIAC Motor Control*

Example Digital Speed Control System for a Motor

Let's suppose that the 8-bit control code has been calibrated to represent a motor speed. It is loaded into a register (the holding register) and is held in temporary storage until the input voltage, V_A, crosses the zero-volt axis. Each time V_A crosses the axis, a zero-crossing detector circuit generates a pulse P_1. For 60-hertz ac power, P_1 is generated every 8.33 milliseconds. P_1 loads the 8-bit code in the holding register into the counter. The counter is increased by 1 (incremented) by the clock pulse. 256 clock pulses occur every 8.33 milliseconds. If the 8-bit code were 00000000 (00_{16}), 255 clock pulses later it would be 11111111 (FF_{16}). When the counter reaches this value, it outputs a pulse that triggers the TRIAC through a pulse transformer. The transformer is used to isolate the high-voltage, high-current TRIAC circuit from the low voltage control circuit. The time that the TRIAC conducts and the average load current is determined by the code loaded into the counter. The circuit timing is shown in *Figure 4-19*.

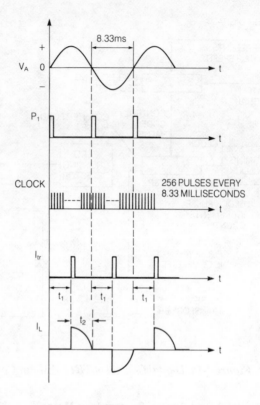

Figure 4-19. *Waveforms from Circuit of Figure 4-18*

For example, if the counter is loaded with a control code equivalent to a decimal value of 254 by P_1, only one clock pulse will be required before the pulse is generated to trigger the TRIAC. The TRIAC will conduct for essentially the full 8.33 milliseconds so the motor operates at full speed. If 0 is loaded into the counter, 255 clock pulses will be required before the gate pulse is generated. This means the TRIAC will be triggered very late in the 8.33 millisecond period and may not be turned on at all. Little or no power will be provided to the motor and the motor speed will be at or near zero. Thus, the motor speed will vary from very slow to full speed as the counter code value is increased from 0 to 255. In *Figure 4-19*, t_1 is the varying time between the occurrence of P_1 and I_{tr} which is determined by the counter code value. This, in turn, determines t_2, the amount of time that the TRIAC conducts and permits load current, I_L, to flow.

Calibrating the Motor Speed

To see how this digital control method works, let's use it to control a furnace blower motor in an air duct. For a particular blower and duct size, the desired motor speed plotted against the air temperature in the duct is shown in *Figure 4-20*. The counter values necessary to obtain particular motor speeds have been determined and are plotted for the motor speed curve as shown in *Figure 4-20*. The data show that the motor should run at 1500 RPM when the duct air temperature is 160°F and that a digital binary code equivalent to 200 pulses should be loaded into the counter.

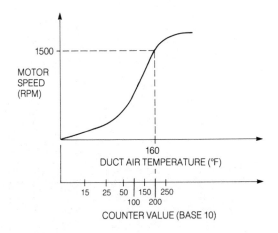

Figure 4-20. *Calibration of Blower Speed Versus Counter Value*

Translating Temperature to Speed

In order to complete the system, some means is required to translate from the temperature in the duct to the counter value. This is accomplished by the system shown in the block diagram of *Figure 4-21*. The values from *Figure 4-20* are placed in a computer system memory and essentially become a look-up table. Let's clarify with the following example:

TEMP	MEMORY ADDRESS	CONTROL CODE	MOTOR SPEED
160°	300_{10}	11001000	1500

The binary code 11001000 is equivalent to the decimal count of 200. It is stored in memory at decimal location 300. Each binary code equivalent for the counts from 0 to 255 are placed in memory in sequence above and below that address.

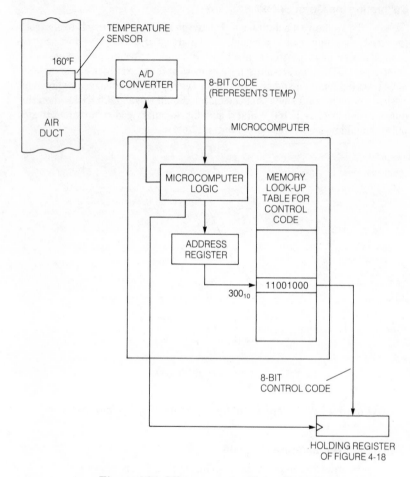

Figure 4-21. *Microcomputer Motor Control*

The control code is looked-up as follows: The temperature sensor continually outputs an analog voltage representing the temperature. When commanded by the microcomputer logic, the A/D converter converts the voltage to an 8-bit digital code corresponding to the temperature. The computer uses an input instruction to input the 8-bit digital code representing the temperature. When this digital code is received, the computer logic decodes it, computes the address of the control code, and outputs the address through the address register to memory. A memory read is performed and control code 11001000 is latched into the holding register by the computer. The control procedure continues as previously discussed to trigger the TRIAC and control the motor speed to 1500 RPM.

Each temperature code has a specific control code associated with it to control the motor to a specific speed for that temperature. The memory is a look-up table, the temperature code is an index, and the computer logic performs the look-up and read functions. The computer samples the air temperature at a regular rate and updates the holding register value each time. If the temperature remains at 160 degrees, the holding register is loaded with 11001000 after each sample. If the temperature changes, the computed address changes to locate the proper control code for the required motor speed, and this new control code value is loaded into the holding register.

This type of sequence is basically an open-loop control system because there is no feedback. The motor speed control system responds to a control variable value (in this case air temperature), and depends on the system calibration to maintain the correct motor speed. The actual motor speed is not monitored by any kind of feedback signal to see if the 1500 RPM motor speed is actually achieved. When feedback is used, it is called a closed loop system.

Closed-Loop System

Figure 4-22 is an example of a closed-loop motor control. The basic difference from *Figure 4-21* is the addition of the motor speed feedback signal to the computer. The motor speed is converted to a voltage by the tachometer and this voltage is converted to a digital code by an A/D converter. The digital code is calibrated to provide the same control code as dictated by *Figure 4-20*.

The microcomputer accomplishes this by decoding the speed digital code and generating the appropriate memory address just as it does for decoding the temperature digital code. Here is the sequence of steps in the control cycle indicated on *Figure 4-22:*

1. The microcomputer requests the A/D converter to sample the temperature.
2. The digital code representing the temperature is sent to the microcomputer.
3. The microcomputer decodes the temperature code and addresses the appropriate control code.
4. The control code is sent to the microcomputer ALU and stored in register B, and also is temporarily stored in register C.
5. The microcomputer requests the A/D converter to sample the motor speed.
6. The digital code representing the speed is sent to the microcomputer.
7. The microcomputer decodes the code and generates an address to locate the control code corresponding to the speed.
8. The control code dictated by the speed code is sent to the microcomputer ALU and stored in register A.

9. The microcomputer ALU compares register A and register B. If A is less than B (as it is in *Figure 4-22*), the register C value is increased by the difference.
10. The microcomputer latches the new code value in register C into the holding register of *Figure 4-18* and the TRIAC control sequence begins.

If the speed had been greater than desired, register A would have been greater than register B and register C would have been decreased by the difference to lower the motor speed. When the desired speed is reached, register A equals register B and register C is not changed. The correction process adjusts the motor speed to reach and stay at the desired value until a new speed is determined because the temperature has changed.

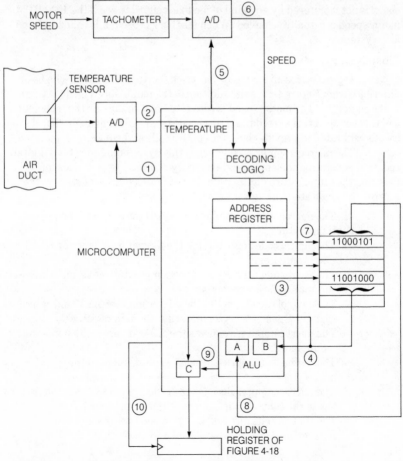

Figure 4-22. Closed-Loop System Motor Control

4

How to Control Motors and Generators

Obviously, the closed loop system is more expensive, because an extra sensor (the tachometer) and another A/D converter are required. For the example application (the furnace blower motor control), such precise speed control is not needed and the simpler open-loop control system would be adequate. In fact, as will be shown in the next chapter, most residential heating systems simply turn on the blower motor with a thermostatic switch when the air duct temperature reaches a minimum temperature. However, for applications where motor speed must be controlled accurately, the control system of *Figure 4-22* can be modified easily to fit those applications.

MOTOR STARTING

One item that has not been stressed in the discussion of motor control is the special condition that occurs when the motor is to be started. The main problem is that when the armature (or rotor) is at a standstill, there is no CEMF and the armature current can be excessive. In fact, a synchronous motor may never start rotating unless some initial rotational energy is provided. Usually this is supplied by providing several closed coil windings to supply an induction motor starting torque. When the armature gains speed, these high resistance coils carry little current due to the CEMF, while the normal armature windings carry the current required to operate the motor at the power level desired. Such internal design features make the motors self-starting and apply equally well to single-phase or three-phase motors.

The starting current in dc and wound-rotor induction motors often is limited by connecting an external resistance in series with the armature windings. As the motor speed increases and builds up CEMF, the resistance is removed and the motor operates normally. The resistance may be controlled manually or can be incorporated into an electronic motor control of the type that has been discussed previously.

One special technique that is applied to single-phase induction motors to make them self starting is shown in *Figure 4-23*. The two field windings are mechanically located 90° apart on the motor housing. A centrifugal switch and a capacitor are connected in series with the one winding called the starting winding. The centrifugal switch is closed when the motor is not running. The capacitor shifts the phase of the current in the starting winding to provide starting torque in the desired direction of rotation. The out-of-phase current causes a distorted magnetic field that provides the starting torque. The centrifugal switch operating mechanism is mounted on the motor shaft. As the motor speed increases, centrifugal force opens the switch which opens the starting circuit. From that point on, motor operation is controlled by the run field winding. The speed can be controlled by field winding current or by the voltage applied to the motor. Such a motor is called a capacitor-start induction motor.

Understanding Electronic Control of Energy Systems

4-27

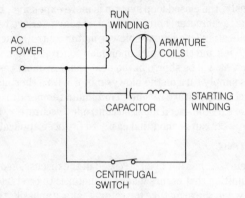

Figure 4-23. *Starting Circuit for a Capacitor Start Induction Motor*

AC POWER TRANSMISSION SYSTEMS

The ac voltage used to power the motors in the motor control systems discussed is delivered to homes and factories over power transmission systems. A basic system is shown in *Figure 4-24*. It consists of power plants that feed the transmission system and an energy management center. The energy management center is the termination point for the SCADA (Supervisory Control and Data Acquisition) system which sends data to the center on the status of voltages, currents, system frequency and the system circuit breakers, and provides the signals necessary to open or close the circuit breakers (supervisory control).

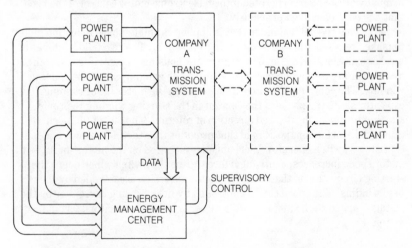

Figure 4-24. *Power Transmission System*

Note, especially, that the transmission system of a particular power company is not independent. It is physically connected to and it feeds and is fed by the transmission system of other power companies. This fact plays an important part of how generators in the power system are controlled. We'll investigate that fact more a little later, but before we do, let's briefly look at the power plant of the overall system.

Power Plant

One may suspect that electronics has little part to play in the operation of a power plant. However, as shown in *Figure 4-25*, electronics plays a big part. Throughout the boiler-turbine-generator system there are five major subsystems controlled by electronics. Starting from the top left and going clockwise, the control subsystems for feedwater, steam pressure, generator voltage, generator frequency and steam temperature all use electronics for control.

Generator Voltage

Let's first look at how the generator voltage and frequency are controlled. The generator voltage output can be increased or decreased by increasing or decreasing the intensity of the magnetic field of the generator. The magnetic field current requirement of this generator is so large that it must be supplied by another generator called an exciter. The field current of the exciter then can be controlled by electronic circuits. The exciter is driven by mounting it on the same shaft as the main generator. If the field current of the exciter is increased or decreased, the exciter output feeding the generator field will be increased or decreased and the generator voltage will be increased or decreased respectively.

A closed-loop is formed by measuring the output voltage of the generator, converting it to a dc voltage, comparing it to a standard voltage with a differential amplifier and letting the output of the differential amplifier control the dc voltage regulator feeding the exciter field current. If the generator voltage increases, the exciter field current is decreased to decrease the generator voltage. The reverse occurs if the generator voltage decreases.

Generator Frequency

The generator frequency is determined by the generator design and by the speed of the turbine that drives the generator. The turbine speed is increased or decreased by regulating the steam feeding the turbine with a hydraulic valve that is controlled electronically. The closed-loop control occurs as follows: The generator frequency is sensed and compared to a frequency standard over a given time, Δt. If the generator frequency is too high, the hydraulic valve is pulsed to reduce the steam flow and reduce the speed. If the generator frequency is too low, the opposite occurs. Note there is an input marked (C) to the pulse driver coming from the energy management center. This is based on a area control signal and is used to change the load on the generator when the system load changes by momentarily changing the generator frequency.

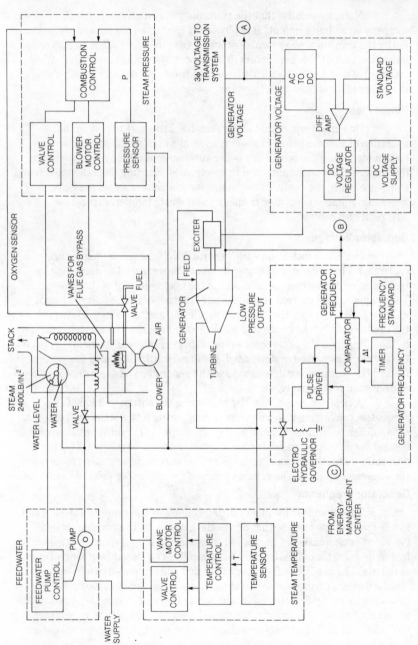

Figure 4-25. *Power Plant*

Steam Pressure

Steam pressure is controlled by varying the amount of blower air and the amount of fuel that is sent to the power plant burners. Circuits similar to the motor control circuits discussed previously are used to control the motors and valves. The combustion control electronics receives inputs from a steam pressure sensor and an oxygen sensor (detects how well the fuel is burned) to regulate the air/fuel mixture to the burner. Too much oxygen indicates inadequate burning; therefore, a need for more fuel. Too high a steam pressure indicates too much air and fuel.

Steam Temperature

Proper steam temperature must be maintained so that the system operates with maximum efficiency and to assure that the turbine and boiler metal are not overheated. If the temperature is too high, either some of the flue gases are bypassed around some of the superheater boiler coils or water is sprayed into the steam to cool off the steam. The steam, of course, remains superheated so that no water enters the turbine and damages it. Motor controls and similar valve controls make up the bulk of the electronics.

Feedwater

One last control subsystem for feedwater completes the five subsystems. The water level in the boiler is maintained to within a close tolerance (like less than an inch) by controlling a pump with a motor or a small steam turbine. The total feedwater system is a closed loop system where the steam from the low pressure side of the turbine is condensed and returned to the water supply that feeds the feedwater pump. This portion of the system is not shown because it would add little to understanding the basic system.

The water level is monitored by a sensor that is a variable resistor voltage divider. As the water level rises, the sensor voltage decreases to lower the average current to the motor driving the pump or reduces the steam to the turbine driving the pump. This reduces the water flow. The opposite occurs if the water level goes down.

All of these control subsystems work as closed loops independently of the other subsystems. Data from some of them, such as the voltage at point (A) and the frequency at point (B), are fed to the energy management center for monitoring or additional control inputs. The main objective is to keep the power transmission system supplied with the necessary power to handle the system load and to supply the power as economically as possible.

Transmission System

Figure 4-26 shows a very simplified typical power company transmission system consisting of two power plants, three substations, a connection to another company's transmission system, some detail on the data collection system back to the energy management center and some detail on the distribution of power to individual customers.

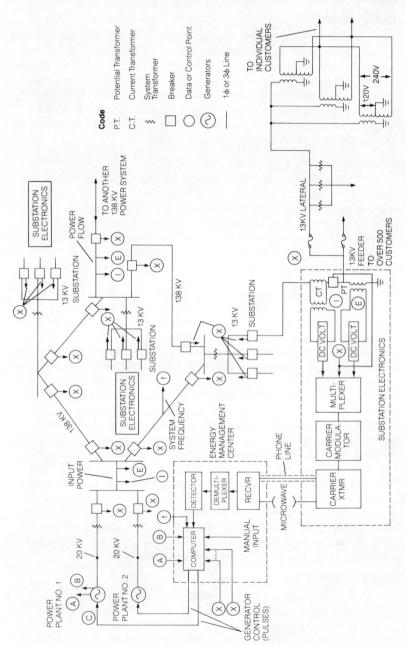

Figure 4-26. Transmission System

The generators at the power plant produce three-phase, 60-hertz, 20,000 (20 KV) volts at their output. Using three-phase transformers with more turns on the secondary than on the primary, the 20 KV is stepped up to 138 KV for transmission around the system. Usually a voltage in the range of 69 KV to 138 KV is used for city transmission and up to 500KV for cross-country transmission.

At the substations (which are the main distribution terminals located as close as possible to the customers), the voltages are stepped down to 13 KV with transformers. From the substations, the power is distributed over feeder lines and stepped down further to the 240 volts and 120 volts used in homes and factories as shown.

In order to transmit power with the highest efficiency (lowest loss), transmission occurs at the highest voltage. For example, if 100,000 volt-amperes is generated, it could be transmitted as 20,000 volts at 5 amperes or 100,000 volts at 1 ampere. Since the power loss due to the wire resistance varies as the square of the line current, (I^2R), the power loss at 5 amperes would be 25 times the power loss at 1 ampere. Of course, the transmission lines for the higher voltage would be more expensive because specially insulated supports, and greater clearance between wires and between wires and tower are required to prevent arcing and current leakage between wires and between an individual wire and ground.

DATA ACQUISITION

The points marked (E) and (I) on *Figure 4-26* are examples of the measurement of voltage and current that exists at particular points in the power system. As shown, the voltage is measured with a potential transformer that steps it down from the transmission line value to a measurement level. The ac voltage is converted to a dc voltage that represents the value of the ac voltage. The current is measured with a current transformer which is magnetically coupled to the current that flows in the power line. The ac voltage at the output of the current transformer is converted to a dc voltage to represent the value of the ac current.

These two measurements, as well as hundreds more, are multiplexed (taken one at a time) in sequence and modulate a signal at a carrier frequency The modulated carrier carrying the information with it is transmitted to the energy management center either over phone lines or by microwave signals.

At the energy management center, the multiplexed signal is sorted out (demultiplexed) into the individual signals, detected and sent to the computer to be used by the computer for monitor information, supervisory control, or for computing area control error. The points marked A and B are the same as the (A) and (B) of *Figure 4-25* and f is the frequency of the power existing on the transmission system.

SUPERVISORY CONTROL

The points marked (X) on *Figure 4-26* are the status and control lines for the system circuit breakers that provide the supervisory control to open or close any breaker in the system either manually or by computer. Breakers may open automatically because of faults on the line, or they may be opened to repair or maintain certain lines. Supervisory control allows the breakers to be opened and closed by remote control to route power over different system paths to go around faults until the faults are repaired. This permits the power company to provide power to its customers with minimum interruption.

AREA CONTROL

Note the points (E) and (I) that are located on the line between the power plants and the input to the transmission system. By measuring these two quantities, the amount of power being delivered to the transmission system can be measured. In a similar fashion, measuring (E) and (I) on the line that is connected to another company's transmission system will determine the amount of interchange power that is occurring between the systems. Interchange can have three conditions. Power is supplied to another company; power is received from another company; or no power is transferred in either direction—interchange is zero. In all cases, the total system in steady state will remain balanced so that all power generated (minus distribution losses) will be used by customers over the network.

In power systems, the load, in most cases, is continually changing. Therefore, the problem of control is to match the generators to the load rather than visa versa. If a power system is operating at steady-state and the load suddenly changes, the equation that governs how the system is controlled to match the load change is as follows:

$$\text{Area Control Error} = (\text{Bias} \times \text{Frequency Error, } (\Delta f)) + \text{Interchange Error, } (\Delta I).$$

The area control error (ACE) represents the needed change in generation that must be made to adjust the system to the load change. In addition, a principle of power system control is that generator frequency change is a direct indication of load changes.

To clarify the terms in the ACE equation, let's refer to *Figure 4-27* to see how the equation is computed. Recall that interchange was defined as the power supplied or received by a transmission system. In *Figure 4-27*, the various interchange connections that are made between the power system in question (Power Company No. 1) and other power systems are monitored to determine if power is being supplied to or received from other power systems. All of the interchange power amounts are computed to arrive at a net interchange value for power. Again, it has three conditions; either a net value supplied, a net value received or zero. If the net interchange value is different from the desired interchange value then there is an interchange error.

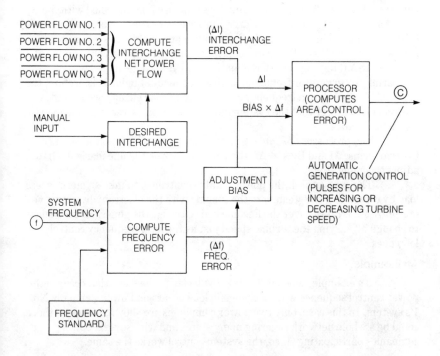

Figure 4-27. Computing Automatic Generation Control

The desired interchange value is put into the system manually because each day the power companies may agree to supply each other set amounts of power. In this case, the interchange value is a specific value other than zero and the interchange error is the power change that occurs from the desired value. Therefore,

Interchange Error = Resultant of actual interchange power and desired interchange power.

If a load change occurs that results in an interchange error, the interchange error is the amount of power that the system must increase or decrease based upon what the net interchange actually is compared to what is desired.

The frequency error shown in *Figure 4-27* is essentially the same thing since a change in generator frequency can be equated to a change in load. However, it is modified by a bias adjustment before it is combined with the interchange error to compute the area control error. The bias is an adjustment factor that determines how much of a system load change the system should handle itself. The bias adjustment multiplies the frequency error to arrive at the (Bias × Δ f) term of the ACE equation. The Δ f is determined by comparing the generator frequency with a frequency standard. Therefore, the bias × Δf is a result of a frequency change when a load change occurs and is the amount of power that the system must increase or decrease based upon the frequency change.

The processor of *Figure 4-27* computes the ACE from the inputs of the two terms, ΔI and Bias × Δf. It outputs pulses on the line marked (C) to adjust the generator.

The generator at the power plant is controlled to take on more or less load by controlling the steam into the turbine with the electrohydraulic valve of *Figure 4-25*. Pulses over the line marked (C) cause the generator frequency to change by varying the turbine speed just as the local frequency control loop does.

An Example

An example shown in *Table 4-1* will clarify the steps that occur in the power control sequence when a change in load occurs on Power Company No. 1's system. In this case, only two power companies are shown; however, there could be a whole network covering many states and with several power companies participating. If so, the system control works the same.

Table 4-1. Control Sequence

	Power Company No. 1				Power Company No. 2			
	GEN. (MW)	LOAD (MW)	(BIAS × Δf) (MW)	ΔI (MW)	GEN. (MW)	LOAD (MW)	(BIAS × Δf) (MW)	ΔI (MW)
Steady State	500	500	0	0	500	500	0	0
Step 1	500	510	8	0	500	500	2	0
Step 2	508	510	0	−2	502	500	0	2
Step 3	510	510	0	0	500	500	0	0

The steady-state condition for both power companies is that they each are generating 500 megawatts for a 500 megawatt load and there is no interchange between them. The frequency is 60-hertz, therefore, there is no Δf. As a result

$$ACE = (Bias \times \Delta f) + \Delta I$$

is

$$0 = 0 + 0.$$

The bias adjustment is set such that the (bias × Δf) term will result in Power Company No. 1 taking 80% of any load change and Power Company No. 2 taking 20% of any load change.

Step 1 is the instant that a load change of 10 megawatts occurs on Power Company No. 1's system. A frequency change from 60-hertz occurs in the system. The computation of (bias × Δf) for No. 1 results in the ACE = 8 for No. 1 and ACE = 2 for No. 2 since ΔI = 0 for this instant. As a result, No. 1's generators are increased to 508 megawatts and No. 2's generators to 502 megawatts. The frequency is restored to 60 hertz; therefore, Δf = 0 as shown in Step 2.

Since No. 2 is supplying No. 1 with 2 megawatts, ΔI = 2 for No. 2 and ΔI = -2 for No. 1. ACE is now -2 for No. 1 and 2 for No. 2 since Δf × 0 as shown in step 2. As a result, the generator for No. 1 is adjusted up to 510 megawatts to take the full load and the generator for No. 2 is adjusted down to 500 megawatts to make ΔI × 0. The two systems are now in a new steady-state condition shown in step 3. No. 1 has picked up the full load change of 10 megawatts, the frequency is 60 hertz, Δf = 0 and ΔI = 0.

WHAT HAVE WE LEARNED?

1. Electrical energy is converted to mechanical energy by motor action. Motor action occurs when current is passed through a coil of wire in a magnetic field.
2. Electronic control of motors has been made practical by using SCRs and TRIACs to replace relay contacts and to vary the power delivered to the motor.
3. The power necessary to run the motors in our homes and factories is supplied over power transmission systems that are supplied by large generators driven by steam or water turbines.
4. A great deal of electronics is used in the power transmission system, both for monitoring and control.

Quiz for Chapter 4

1. In a motor winding with current flowing through it, the force on the winding is in a direction:
  a. toward the weaker magnetic field.
  b. perpendicular to the wire.
  c. perpendicular to the plane of the wire.
  d. all of the above.
  e. a and b above.

2. A commutator is used:
  a. in dc motors only.
  b. in motors requiring current in only one direction in the winding.
  c. to control the direction of the current in the armature windings.
  d. all of the above.

3. Counter EMF is:
  a. developed in the armature winding due to generator action.
  b. developed in the same direction as the applied voltage.
  c. developed in the opposite direction as the applied voltage.
  d. tends to increase motor speed.
  e. tends to decrease motor speed.
  f. a, c, and e above.
  g. a, b, and d above.

4. A 240 VRMS sinusoidal signal has a peak voltage of about:
  a. 240
  b. 269
  c. 300
  d. 340

5. The motor action in a three-phase motor is caused by:
  a. a rotating magnetic field produced by the field windings.
  b. a rotating magnetic field produced by the rotor windings.
  c. a steady magnetic field produced by the field windings.

6. A synchronous motor is:
  a. a dc motor with variable speed control.
  b. an ac motor with variable speed control.
  c. an ac motor whose speed is fixed within narrow limits by its design.
  d. an ac motor whose rotor winding current continually reverses.

7. The torque of an ac induction motor at its maximum speed is:
  a. zero.
  b. at its maximum value.
  c. at one-half its maximum value.

8. The torque of an ac induction motor maximizes at:
  a. full speed.
  b. near full speed.
  c. at about one-half full speed.
  d. when the rotor is still.

9. A suppressor diode is used in a digital relay driver circuit to:
  a. suppress the arc across the power contacts.
  b. speed up the switching action of the relay coil.
  c. protect the digital circuit from current spikes.
  d. protect the digital circuit from large voltage spikes.

10. The SCR or TRIAC replaces which component in a motor control circuit?
  a. suppressor diode
  b. relay coil
  c. current limiting resistor
  d. relay or switch

11. In order for an SCR to turn on:
  a. the anode voltage must be positive with respect to the cathode.
  b. the cathode voltage must be positive with respect to the anode.
  c. the gate must be pulsed with a positive current that is above the threshold level.
  d. the gate must be held at zero volts.
  e. a and c above.
  f. b and c above.

How to Control Heating and Air Conditioning Systems

ABOUT THIS CHAPTER

In the mid-1970's, about 20 percent of the energy used in the United States was for heating and air conditioning residential and commercial buildings. Since such a large portion of energy is used for this purpose, it is important that it be used efficiently. Improved construction methods and insulation can help. A relatively new way to help conserve energy is to control heating and air conditioning equipment with electronic control systems. Proper use of such systems can significantly reduce the energy costs of home and business heating and air conditioning.

In this chapter, the basic operation and control of heating and cooling systems are presented for general knowledge, then the use of electronic controls are discussed.

FUNDAMENTALS OF HEATING

Sources of Heat

The main sources of heat for present heating systems are the combustible fuels (coal, oil and gas), electric heat and the heat pump. In some areas, wood might also be considered a major source of home heating. These are the ones covered in this chapter. Solar collectors are becoming more important as a heat source and a later chapter is devoted to solar energy. However, some of the distribution and control methods presented in this chapter are applicable to solar heating systems.

Transfer of Heat

Natural heat transfer is always from a higher temperature to a lower temperature just as the natural flow of water is from a higher elevation to a lower elevation. Heat transfer can occur by one or more of three means: (1) convection, (2) radiation, and (3) conduction. These are illustrated in *Figure 5-1.*

TYPES OF HEATING SYSTEMS

The types of heating systems are based on the three types of heat transfer. However, most heating systems utilize more than one of the heat transfer types. Also, different methods may be used to accomplish any one type of heat transfer. Some of the more common methods will be discussed.

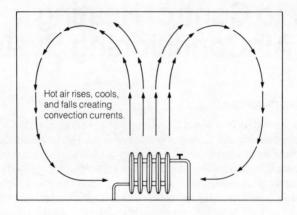

a. Convection

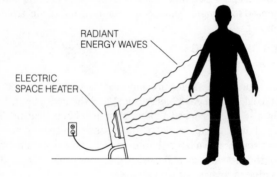

b. Radiation

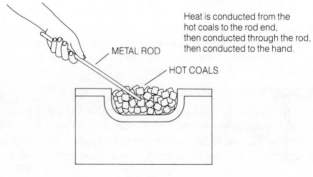

c. Conduction

Figure 5-1. Heat Transfer Methods

Convection Heating

The steam or hot water heating system is an example of convection heating. A heat source heats water to boiling to produce steam or to below boiling for the hot water system. The steam system has two advantages over the hot water system. First, the steam carries much more heat and second, if the boiler is at a low point in the building, the steam will rise to the radiators and the condensed steam (water) will flow back to the boiler without the pump that is required to circulate the hot water in the hot water system.

Radiant Heating

The two most common types of radiant heating systems have the heat source in the ceiling or floor. In the ceiling heat system, an insulated electrical resistance wire is distributed over the entire ceiling of each room and covered with a thin layer of finishing material to conceal it. The heat from the wire radiates into the room. One advantage of this system is the ease of room control since the wire for each room may be switched on and off separately.

In the floor heat system, hot heat is circulated by a pump through pipes in the floor material, such as concrete, which heats the floor. Then the entire floor radiates heat into the room. This system has the advantage of heating the lowest part of the room first which, of course, is where the cooler air collects.

Conduction Heating

The direct heating of air and the forced circulation of the heated air by a fan or blower in the forced air furnace is probably the most common method of heating.

Figure 5-2 shows a simplified diagram of such a system. The blower, driven by an electric motor, draws in air through a filter which removes much of the dust from the air. The air then passes through a heat exchanger which is heated by the heat source. The source of heat for the system may be any practical source. Typically it is from the combustion of wood, coal, oil or gas, but it may be from electrical resistance, the condenser coil of a heat pump, or a solar collector.

The air is heated by conduction from the heat exchanger and passes through ducts to the rooms or areas to be heated. The heated air from the ducts heats objects in the room by conduction. As the air gives up its heat, it cools and is pulled from the room through a cold air return to the furnace by the blower suction. The air is filtered, reheated and the cycle repeats.

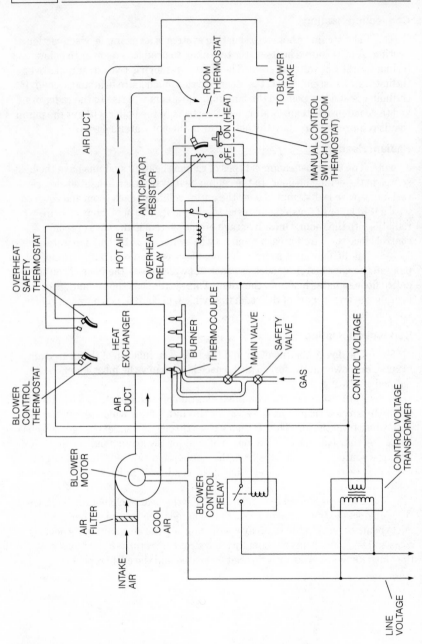

Figure 5-2. *Gas-Fired Forced Air Furnace*

In this example, only the air present in the area is recirculated because it is a closed-loop system. In a residential building, this is satisfactory because the normal opening of outside doors and the leakage around doors and windows throughout the house admit enough fresh air. However, in energy efficient construction where air leakage is minimized and in large commercial buildings, the air in the closed-loop system will become stale and excessively dry. Methods to mix a small amount of outside air with the recirculated air will be discussed later in this chapter.

Heat Exchanger

Open Flame Type

The heat exchanger for a forced air furnace is required when the heat source is a combustible fuel in order to separate the smoke and fumes in the combustion chamber from the circulated air. The heat exchanger is not required for electrical resistance heating since there is no open flame or direct burning.

The basic structure of this type heat exchanger is shown in *Figure 5-3*. It is constructed so that a large surface area of the hot metal can be in contact with the air to be heated. The "inside" of the heat exchanger, the combustion chamber, is designed to contain most of the heat so it will not be lost out the exhaust vent (flue). The smoke and fumes are guided by the flue to the atmosphere. Notice that the exchanger must be sealed to prevent leakage of the fumes through the exchanger walls into the circulated air.

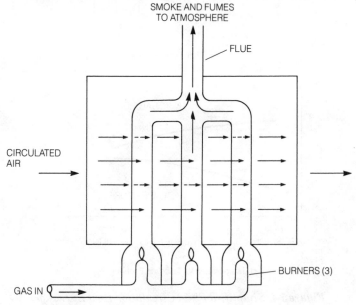

Figure 5-3. Simplified Open Flame Heat Exchanger

Fluid Circulation Type

Another type of heat exchanger is shown in *Figure 5-4a*. This type is used where the heat source is a hot fluid that passes through the tubes or pipes of the exchanger. The hot fluid may be hot water or a special chemical fluid. The hot fluid is labeled fluid 2 in the diagram. Another fluid such as air, fluid 1, passes through the exchanger and makes contact with the tubes. A series of baffles guide the flow of fluid 1 so that it contacts the tubes many times as it passes from the inlet to the outlet. The tube itself may follow a zigzag or coiled path to provide more surface area. In some designs, the tubing is in direct contact with the exchanger walls to heat the walls. This adds more surface area.

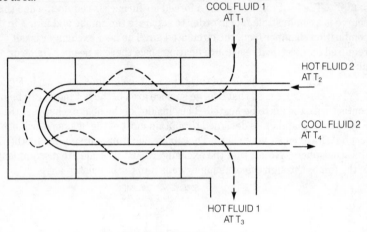

a. Fluid Paths in Exchanger

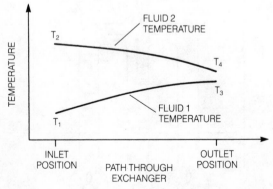

b. Temperature Variations in Exchanger

Figure 5-4. *Simplified Fluid Circulation Heat Exchanger*

The net result is that heat is transferred from fluid 2 to fluid 1 as shown graphically in *Figure 5-4b*. Fluid 1 enters the exchanger at a low temperature T_1 while fluid 2 enters the tube at a high temperature T_2. As the two fluids flow through the structure, fluid 1's temperature increases while fluid 2's temperature decreases. At the outlets of the exchanger, fluid 2's temperature has dropped to T_4 while fluid 1's temperature has increased to T_3. Thus, heat has been exchanged from fluid 2 to fluid 1. Ideally, T_3 would be equal to T_4, but such perfect transfer is not possible. However, as long as T_3 is high enough for the application, the exchanger is acceptable. Further, if T_4 is not much lower than T_2, then the amount of heat that must be added to fluid 2 at the heat source can be held within reasonable limits.

Heat Pump

The heat pump can be the heat source for a forced air heating system. As such, the condenser coil is placed in the circulated air stream as shown in *Figure 5-5*. The condenser coil acts as a heat exchanger of the type discussed in *Figure 5-4*.

The heat pump works on the refrigeration principle that will be discussed in the section on cooling systems. For cooling, the coil in the air stream of *Figure 5-5* cools the air by extracting heat from it. For heating, the refrigerant flow is changed and the functions of the two coils are reversed. Heat is drawn from the outside environment in the evaporator coil and the heat is given up in the condenser coil to the circulated air. This is an important difference from the other heat sources; that is, heat is not generated by the heat pump itself. The heat pump energy is used only to perform work on a fluid. Because of this difference, a heat pump is more efficient than electrical resistance or combustible fuel heat sources.

The evaporator coil is normally exposed to the outside air. It may seem a little strange to think of getting heat from air at a temperature of 40°F since we think of that as cold air. However, 40°F outside air can still be cooled, and as it is, heat is extracted from it by the heat pump. The colder the outside air, the harder the heat pump must work to extract heat. In very cold climates, the evaporator coil may be buried deep in the earth where the temperature is relatively constant at about 50°F year round. Other systems may use water from a deep well whose temperature also is around 50°F to supply heat to the evaporator. Still another method is to use a solar collector to heat the evaporator.

Since the heat pump must work harder to heat a building when the outside temperature is colder, it takes a longer time to raise the inside temperature. Therefore, some heat pump systems have an electrical resistance heater in the circulated air stream along with the condenser coil. This heater is switched on to supplement the heat pump when very cold temperatures are present or when the space needs to be heated quickly.

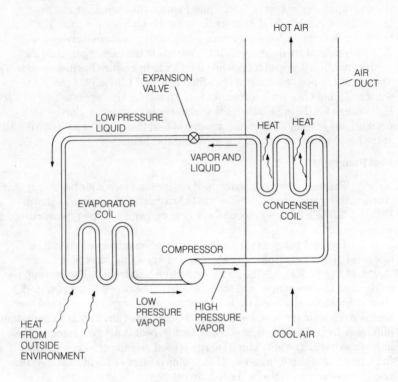

Figure 5-5. Heat Pump System

HEATING SYSTEM CONTROL

The fundamental control function that must be performed in any heating system is that of turning the system on and off. When the room temperature is below the desired temperature set by the system operator, the heating system must be turned on and the flow of hot air, hot water or steam turned on to the room. Similarly, when the room temperature is equal to or above the desired temperature, the system must be turned off.

Thermostat

The device used to provide the temperature sensing and control function is called a thermostat. A thermostat commonly used for residential heating systems has a bimetallic thermal switch as one of its main components.

Bimetallic Strip Thermostat

The basic bimetallic thermal switch is illustrated in *Figure 5-6*. The strip of metal is called a bimetallic strip because it actually consists of two different metals that are bonded together for their entire length. Its operation depends on the fact that materials expand when they are heated and the rate of expansion depends on the material. Thus, when two different metals bonded together in a strip are heated, the length of one metal (metal 1 in *Figure 5-6a*) will increase faster than the length of the second metal (metal 2 in *Figure 5-6a*) causing the strip to bend. If the strip is securely fastened at one end (point A in *Figure 5-6a*), the other end will move in the direction of the slower expanding metal.

An electrical contact fastened to the free end forms a switch with a fixed contact. When the room temperature is below the temperature set on the thermostat as shown in *Figure 5-6a*, the contacts are touching to complete an electrical control circuit which turns on the heating system. As the room temperature increases, the strip bends away from the other contact as shown in *Figure 5-6b* and opens the electrical control circuit. The control circuit then turns off the appropriate part of the heating system. As the room temperature drops, the strip returns to the position of *Figure 5-6a* and the sequence repeats to maintain the average room temperature at the thermostat setting.

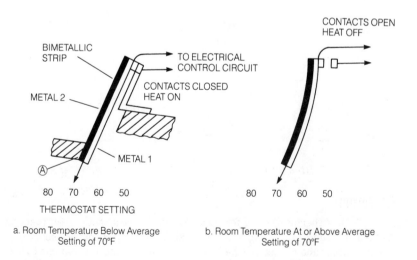

a. Room Temperature Below Average
Setting of 70°F

b. Room Temperature At or Above Average
Setting of 70°F

Figure 5-6. *Bimetallic Strip Thermostat Operation*

The bimetallic strip in some thermostats is formed into a spiral coil as shown in *Figure 5-7*. One end of the coil is attached to a mercury switch while the other end is securely fastened to a backing plate. The backing plate is rotated to set the desired temperature and this changes the position of the mercury switch with respect to the horizontal level position. As the room temperature rises, the coil "winds" tighter and moves the mercury switch past the level position so that the drop of mercury moves to the other end of the glass bulb. The mercury bridges the two contacts and completes the electrical control circuit, or the movement of the mercury might break the circuit if the contacts had been on the other end of the bulb. This type of thermostat is more sensitive to temperature changes than the one of *Figure 5-6*. Also, the *Figure 5-6* thermostat contacts are exposed to dust in the air and are subject to erosion by the arc produced when they open and close. The mercury switch contacts are enclosed within the glass bulb and do not erode.

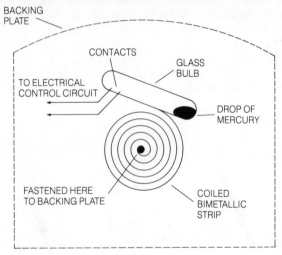

Figure 5-7. *Bimetallic Coiled Strip Thermostat with Mercury Switch*

Anticipator

Most thermostats for forced air systems have an anticipator function. As the name suggests, this function looks ahead to the fact that the set temperature is about to be reached and causes the thermostat contacts to open before the room temperature is actually reached. This is done because only the heat source is shut off when the thermostat contacts open. The blower continues to force air through the hot heat exchanger so that the room temperature continues rising after the thermostat contacts open. The room temperature may overshoot the set temperature a small amount, but without the anticipator, the overshoot amount would be much larger.

The anticipator usually consists of a small resistance heating element located near the bimetallic strip (*Figure 5-2*). Current that flows through the blower control relay also flows through this element and causes it to get warm. This makes the bimetallic strip sense a slightly warmer temperature than the actual room temperature; thus, the thermostat contacts open early enough to prevent a large overshoot.

Set-Back Thermostat

The simple thermostat of *Figure 5-6* is adequate for systems that must respond to only one control temperature in one location of a building on a 24-hour basis. This may not be an energy efficient strategy if the building is not occupied and not in use for long time periods. During such periods, there is no need to heat the building to the same temperature required when it is in use. For these situations, it is desirable to automatically control the heating system to reduce the maintained temperature (or possibly completely turn off the heat) if the period of non-use is relatively long. A type of thermostat called a set-back thermostat can be used to accomplish this function.

Set-back thermostats are used commonly in commercial buildings, but they can be used in the home as well. During the time of day when everyone is at work or school, the temperature of the house can be reduced to a lower level than when people are active in the house. Similarly, when the occupants of the house are asleep under blankets, it is possible to maintain the house at a lower temperature.

Even though this can be done manually, it is much more convenient to have it done automatically. This is especially true on cold mornings, because the thermostat will switch to the higher temperature setting, turn on the heat, and have the house warm before the people get out of bed. The set-back thermostat is designed to perform this operation automatically at the times set by the occupant. In the mechanical version, the thermostat has a clock mechanism which the user sets to control the period of time each temperature setting is to be used. The clock mechanism then mechanically adjusts the position of the bimetallic strip to correspond to the temperature setting for that period of time. This is a very effective control, but the electronic set-back thermostat offers better control of the heating system for even more improved performance. We'll discuss an electronic thermostat and its benefits in a moment, but first let's look at a total heating control system.

TYPICAL HEATING CONTROL SYSTEM

Although the details of the control system are different for different types of heating systems, they all have the general requirements for controlling the heat source, controlling the flow of the heat transfer fluid (air, water, or steam) and monitoring all operations for safety. These requirements can be illustrated by considering a typical gas-fired, forced-air heating system shown in *Figure 5-2*. The fuel flow to the furnace burners and the power to the blower motor are what is to be controlled. The control elements are the room and heat exchanger thermostats, the pilot thermocouple, and their associated relays and valves.

Heat Controls

The control voltage transformer steps down the main electrical line voltage to a low voltage, usually 24 volts, for safety. In *Figure 5-2*, the manual control switch is ON and the room thermostat contacts are closed (requesting heat). This applies control voltage through the normally closed contacts of the overheat relay to operate (open) the main gas control valve. The pilot flame is burning so the safety valve in the gas line is open. When the main control valve is opened, gas flows into the burner and is lit by the pilot flame. As the heat exchanger gets hotter, the blower control thermostat contacts move closer together and eventually close. This energizes the blower control relay with control voltage and current flows through the anticipator resistor in the room thermostat. The blower motor receives power through the blower control relay contacts and the blower circulates hot air to the room. (Of course, the one room shown in this example represents all the rooms in the house).

The heated air causes the temperature in the room to rise and, along with the heat from the anticipator resistor, causes the room thermostat contacts to open. This interrupts the control voltage to close the main gas valve and the burner goes out. The blower continues to run because the heat exchanger is still hot and the blower control thermostat contacts are still closed. The heat exchanger gradually cools, the blower control thermostat contacts open, the blower control relay is de-energized and the blower motor is turned off. Now the room is not being supplied heated air so the room air temperature gradually drops until the room thermostat contacts close. When they do, the cycle repeats.

Safety Controls

The overheat safety thermostat contacts normally never close. However, if the heat exchanger temperature exceeds a safe limit, the contacts close and apply control voltage to energize the overheat relay. This opens the circuit to the main gas valve which closes the valve and shuts off the burner regardless of the room temperature. Conditions which might cause an overheated heat exchanger are: (1) room thermostat contacts stuck closed, (2) blower motor or blower control circuit malfunction so blower doesn't run, or (3) insufficient air flow due to clogged air filter or blocked intake register.

The safety valve in the gas supply line is normally open when the pilot flame is on. This valve and thermocouple are arranged in a fail-safe combination so that the pilot flame must be on in order for the valve to be open. The thermocouple consists of two wires of different materials that are twisted together at the ends. When one junction is heated by the pilot flame, an electrical voltage is generated. This voltage controls the safety valve and holds it open as long as the thermocouple junction is hot. If the pilot flame goes out, the thermocouple current decreases and the safety valve closes. This shuts off the gas supply to both the burner and the pilot light so that raw gas cannot escape into the house. To light the pilot, a special bypass valve must be manually held open while it is being lit and until the pilot flame heats the thermocouple and energizes the safety valve.

Some systems use an electric spark generator rather than a flame to ignite the burner gas. This method is safer and more energy efficient since the pilot flame consumes gas even when no heat is required.

FUNDAMENTALS OF COOLING

Cooling a surface, material, or area involves the same fundamentals as heating; that is, transfer of heat by conduction, convection, and radiation. Recall that as heat is transferred, one object or fluid becomes warmer (gains heat) while the other object or fluid becomes cooler (loses heat). For forced air heating, the heat from some source is transferred to the inside air and from the inside air to objects in the heated space by the air. For cooling, the heat from the objects in the cooled space is transferred to the inside air and from the inside air to the outside air by way of another fluid. This is accomplished, as for heating, with heat exchangers.

Liquid-Vapor Transformation

Another fundamental of heating and cooling is that of liquid-vapor transformation; that is, evaporation and condensation. *Figure 5-8* illustrates the evaporation and condensation principles. As shown in *Figure 5-8a*, when enough heat is absorbed by a liquid, such as water, the liquid changes to vapor and the evaporator surface becomes cooler due to the heat loss. The reverse of this process is illustrated in *Figure 5-8b*. When water vapor in air strikes a cooler surface, the vapor gives up heat to the surface and condenses into the liquid form so the air becomes cooler and the condenser surface becomes warmer. Of course, liquids other than water act the same way, but the liquid-vapor transformation occurs at different temperatures for different liquids. The operating pressure also affects the transformation temperature.

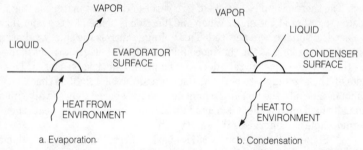

Figure 5-8. *Principles of Heating and Cooling Using Liquid
Vapor Transformations*

TYPES OF COOLING SYSTEMS

The two most commonly used cooling systems are the chilled water system and the refrigeration system. Both use the evaporation-condensation principles. The chilled water system, of course, uses cold water and the refrigeration system uses a special liquid. Let's take the chilled water system first.

Chilled Water System

The chilled water system is relatively simple in concept. Chilled water is pumped through water pipes or tubes that are formed into a coil to increase the area of cold surface. The coil is the heat exchanger and it is placed in the air duct (or plenum) of a forced air system as shown in *Figure 5-9*. The warm room air is filtered and blown through the heat exchanger. Heat from the air is absorbed by the cold water and the cooled air is blown to the room or space to be cooled. Water enters the coil at a cold temperature T_1 and leaves at a warmer temperature T_2. Since the water vapor in the warm room air gives up its heat, the vapor condenses to water on the coil; thus, the air to the room has a lower relative humidity which increases the cooling capability of the air for people. The water drips off the coil into the condensate collector pan and this water is drained away.

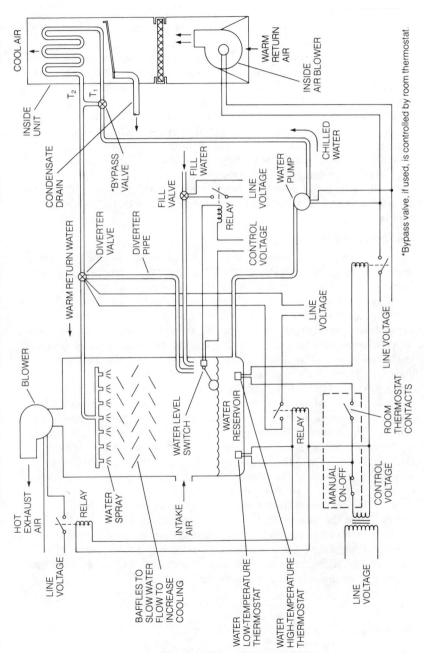

*Bypass valve, if used, is controlled by room thermostat.

***Figure 5-9.** Simplified Chilled Water System*

The source of the chilled water may be a cooling tower type of heat exchanger as shown in *Figure 5-9*. The warm return water at temperature T_2 from the heat exchanger in the duct is sprayed from the top of the tower downward over a system of baffles. The spray breaks up the water into small droplets to aid the cooling process and the baffles slow the fall of the water to allow more time for cooling. Outside air is pulled from near the bottom up through the tower by a blower on top. The moving air through the water evaporates some of the water and cools the water as it falls to the reservoir. The chilled water at temperature T_1 is then pumped back to the heat exchanger in the air duct. Since some of the water evaporates and the resulting water vapor is carried out by the air flow in the tower, some water must be added periodically to the system.

Another way to cool the water or to directly cool the air in the duct is to pass it over an evaporator coil of a refrigeration system. Let's look at this system next.

Refrigeration System

There are two main types of refrigeration systems. One type uses a heat source to heat a refrigerant and the refrigerant flow occurs by convection. Because of this, the system must be level. Natural gas refrigeration systems are of this type because they burn the gas for the heat source. Fuel oil also can be used. This type of system is often used where electricity is not readily available or the cost of electricity is much higher than fuel oil or gas. However, the predominant refrigeration system is one that uses a compressor driven by an electric motor. This is the type chosen for discussion and a simplified diagram is shown in *Figure 5-10*.

The refrigerant in this system is a specially formulated chemical compound, monochlorodifluoromethane, commonly known as Freon®. When the system is not on, the refrigerant exists in the system as a low pressure gas. When cooling is needed, the compressor is turned on and the low pressure gas is compressed to a high-pressure, high-temperature gas. This is done so that the gas will condense at the high outside air temperature that usually exists when cooling is needed. The pressure causes the gas to flow to the condenser coil which is located in the outside air.

The condenser coil is a heat exchanger and heat from the coil is transferred to the outside air. Even though the outside air may be above 120°F, the high-pressure, high-temperature gas condenses in the coil and transfers heat to the outside air. Usually an electric fan blows air over the condenser coil while the compressor is running to improve the heat transfer. Some systems also run cool water over the condenser coil.

®Freon is a registered trademark of E.I. DuPont De Nemours & Co., Inc.

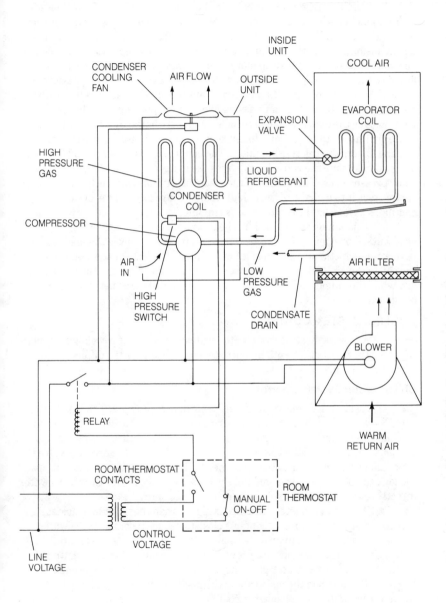

Figure 5-10. *Simplified Refrigeration System*

As the refrigerant gas cools in the condenser, most of it condenses into a liquid. This liquid-gas mixture flows to the evaporator coil which is the heat exchanger in the air duct that circulates the room air. Most systems use an expansion valve in the line just before it enters the evaporator coil which allows the gas pressure to drop more. This changes the remaining gas to a liquid so that the refrigerant entering the evaporator coil is a low pressure liquid. This condition permits the refrigerant to vaporize easily as it absorbs heat from the warm return air passing over the evaporator coil. The air passing over the evaporator coil is cooled and distributed by a blower to the space that needs to be cooled. Moisture in the air condenses on the evaporator coil and lowers the relative humidity. The condensate is collected and drained away. By the time the refrigerant leaves the evaporator coil, it has changed to a low pressure gas. The suction of the compressor pulls this gas back and compresses it to a high-pressure, high-temperature gas and the cycle continues as long as the compressor is running.

This same cycle is used in a heat pump. However, for the heat cycle, as discussed previously for *Figure 5-5*, the refrigerant flow is changed to reverse the functions of the "inside" and "outside" coils. For the heat cycle, the coil in the air duct is the condenser coil and gives off heat to the circulated air, while the outside coil is the evaporator coil and absorbs heat from the outside air.

COOLING SYSTEM CONTROL

As for the heating system, the primary control for a cooling system is the room thermostat. The other control elements vary for the different types of cooling systems.

Chilled Water System Control

A simplified control diagram is shown in *Figure 5-9*. The ON (COOL) —OFF manual switch on the room thermostat is ON. If the water in the cooling tower is not cool enough, the water low-temperature thermostat contacts are closed, so the tower blower is turned on and the diverter valve is set to allow return water to the spray heads. If the water temperature drops too low, the blower is turned off and the diverter valve routes the return water directly to the water reservoir rather than to the spray heads.

When the room temperature is higher than the room thermostat setting, the room thermostat contacts close to request cooling. If the water temperature is too high to provide cooling, the water high-temperature thermostat contacts are open to prevent the water pump from circulating water. Otherwise, the water pump begins circulating the water through the heat exchanger coil in the air duct and the inside air blower is turned on. The warm return water is cooled in the cooling tower and drops to the reservoir for recirculation. When the water level drops due to evaporation during the tower cooling, the water level switch closes and opens the fill valve until the proper reservoir level is established. When the room temperature has cooled enough, the room thermostat contacts open to stop the water pump and inside blower.

The heat exchanger bypass valve may be used in systems where two or more heat exchangers are used for zone control. If one zone does not need cooling while others do, the bypass valve is turned on for the cool zone.

Refrigeration System Control

The simplified control diagram for a refrigeration system is shown in *Figure 5-10*. Notice that this control system is less complex than that for the chilled water system. For cooling, the manual ON/OFF switch is closed in the ON position. When the room thermostat calls for cooling by its closed contacts, the control relay (actually more than one is used) turns on the compressor, condenser fan, and inside blower all at the same time. No delay is needed for the inside blower since cooling starts in a few seconds. The refrigeration cycle continues as previously described until the room temperature cools to the set level. The room thermostat contacts open and the entire system is turned off at the same time. Although the evaporator coil is still cold at shut off, it doesn't remain cold enough for a long enough time to do any significant cooling; therefore, the blower is turned off without a delay time. When the temperature in the space to be cooled rises to the point that the room thermostat contacts close again, the cycle repeats.

The high pressure switch is a safety device to turn off the system if the refrigerant pressure is too high. It also prevents immediate restart after turn off because the compressor would be overloaded if it tried to start up against the high pressure. About two or three minutes are required for the system pressure to equalize after compressor turn off.

If the refrigeration system is used to provide chilled water, the room thermostat is replaced by a water temperature thermostat of the chilled water system. Of course, water flows over the evaporator coil rather than air.

Air Mixing and Zone Control

In the section on heating systems, it was mentioned that sometimes it is desirable to mix fresh outside air with the recirculated air. This improves the air quality by increasing the oxygen-to-carbon dioxide ratio, raising the relative humidity (desirable for heating), and removing the odors that build up in a tightly closed building.

Basic Mixing

The basic method of mixing outside air with return air is shown in *Figure 5-11*. Damper flaps are placed in the return air duct and the outside air duct. The proportions of fresh air and recirculated air in the filtered air mixture are determined by the relative positions of the dampers. In some systems, these dampers may be manually controlled, but in most modern systems they are automatically operated by electric motors or vacuum motors which are controlled by an electronic control system. As fresh air is brought in, an air-pressure relief vent in the system (not shown) permits some air to escape.

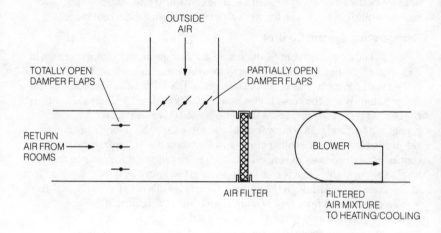

Figure 5-11. *Basic Outside Air Mixing*

Dual-Duct Mixing

Figure 5-12 illustrates the concept of mixing heated and cooled air in a dual-duct system where both heating and cooling systems operate simultaneously. Each room or zone along the length of the main ducts is connected to both ducts through a converging duct. The two room control dampers are set to provide the desired proportions of heated and cooled air to the room. Again, control of the dampers may be manual or automatic. When automatic, the damper positions are controlled via the room thermostat.

Reheat Method

The reheat method of temperature control is shown in *Figure 5-13*. The air in the main duct is always cooled by a cooling system and distributed throughout the building. The branch duct to each room or zone contains a heating coil usually heated by a hot water system. The temperature of the main duct cool air is maintained at a temperature low enough to provide adequate cooling if that is what is desired. If a warmer temperature is needed in a particular room or zone, the hot water is allowed to circulate through that room or zone's heating coil to reheat the air. The bypass valve for the heating coil is controlled by the room thermostat.

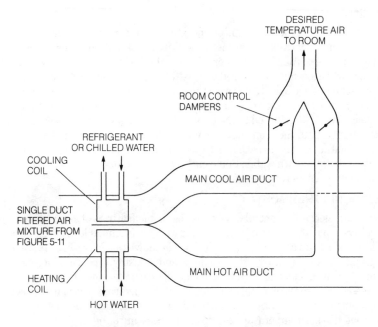

Figure 5-12. Dual-Duct Heating and Cooling System

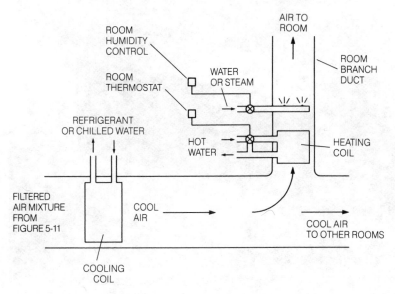

Figure 5-13. Reheat Air Method

Humidity Control

The reheat method of air temperature control removes more moisture from the air than other methods. Because of this, some means of adding moisture to the air is often provided in the system. In other cases, additional moisture may be desired because of health or geographic reasons. Various schemes are used to increase the moisture (relative humidity) in the air. In *Figure 5-13*, a water pipe sprays either a water mist or steam into the air stream as it is distributed to the room. The humidity control senses the relative humidity in the room air and controls the water flow into the air stream. Another common method is to pass the air stream over or through a material saturated with water. Some of the water evaporates into the air stream and raises its relative humidity.

ELECTRONIC THERMOSTAT

An electronic control device that has some features of a computer control system is the electronic thermostat with programmable temperature set-back and set-up capability. A typical one is shown in *Figure 5-14*. It is a useful and convenient device for both home and industry. The use of set-back thermostats using electric clocks and bimetallic strip thermostats was discussed earlier in the chapter, but the use of the electronic thermostat makes the system much more versatile. It not only has a wider range of set-back times, but also has temperature set-up capabilities and offers more control options.

Figure 5-14. *Digital Thermostat*

The programmability and versatility offered by computer control is indicated by the features of this microcomputer controlled thermostat. The unit offers keyboard programming and visual display of up to six different control times and seven temperatures with up to four different time and temperature settings possible for any given 24-hour period. In contrast, electromechanical set-back thermostats offer only two temperature and time settings and the mechanical setting of the times and temperatures are much less precise. Further, the microcomputer controlled version has a digital display which shows the time or temperature when requested at the keyboard.

The unit has an internal lock-out timer to prevent restart of the heating or cooling system for a few minutes after the system has just completed a heating or cooling cycle. This prevents the system from turning on and off too often because it is inefficient and could damage a refrigerant cooling system compressor. The unit has battery backup so that the clock time and programmed schedule will not be lost from the computer memory even if house power is interrupted. If the battery power also fails, the system automatically resets to 72°F when the house power is restored. All of these features contribute to the cost effectiveness and convenience of use of the electronic version of the room thermostat.

System Operation

The connection of the electronic thermostat to the heating and cooling system is as shown in *Figure 5-15*. The unit can be installed as easily as the conventional type of thermostat. The operating current for the thermostat is obtained from the 24-volt control transformer. When the system is heating, the current for the electronics is supplied through the cooling contactor. When the system is cooling, it is supplied through the heating valve solenoid. The small amount of current delivered to the thermostat electronics through either coil is not enough to cause the contactor or the gas valve to actuate.

When in the HEAT mode and heating is required, the heating valve solenoid is energized by the thermostat electronics by turning ON the solid-state electronic switch (TRIAC). When in the COOL mode and cooling is required, the cooling contactor is energized by the thermostat electronics by turning ON the same TRIAC. The TRIAC acts like mechanical switch contacts; thus, when it is ON it has a low resistance and allows enough current flow to actuate the heating valve or the cooling contactor. When it is OFF, it acts like an open circuit.

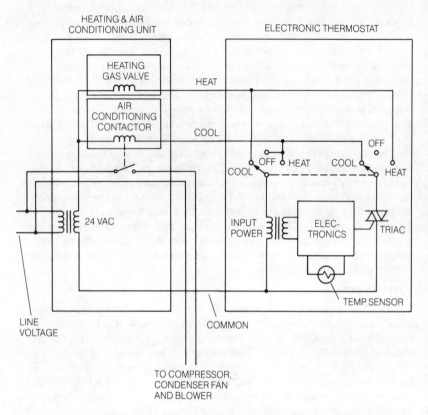

Figure 5-15. *Simplified Connection Diagram for the Electronic Thermostat*

Temperature Sensing

The room temperature-sensing element is not a bimetal thermal switch with contacts, but a solid-state electronic sensor whose resistance varies with temperature. The variations in resistance produce a signal that tells the thermostat electronics to turn ON or turn OFF the TRIAC. Room temperatures below the HEAT or above the COOL reference temperature produce signals that turn ON the TRIAC. Room temperatures at or above the HEAT or at or below the COOL reference temperature produce signals that turn OFF the TRIAC

However, the sensor signal temperature is not the only input to determine if the TRIAC is to be turned ON or OFF. The set-back or set-up times and temperatures which are entered by the operator through the thermostat keyboard, as well as the internal program stored in the microcomputer, contribute to the decision about the state of the TRIAC. Let's examine how this is done in more detail.

Thermostat Electronics

Figure 5-16 is a block diagram of the electronic thermostat. Let's correlate the blocks with the picture of *Figure 5-14*. The external inputs to the system come from the control switches labeled "SYSTEM", "FAN" and "MODE"; from the keyboard keys for "TIME", "TEMP" and numbers; and from the solid-state room temperature sensor. The system outputs are time and temperature readings on the light-emitting diode (LED) display and the control of the TRIAC solid-state electronic switch.

As seen in *Figure 5-16*, the heart of the system is the microcomputer. It receives the external inputs from the system control switches, the keyboard keys, and the room temperature sensor. It receives an internal input from an electronic counter circuit that keeps track of the time of day after being properly set by the operator. All of these signals are in digital form. That is, they are a combination of discrete electrical signals that represent bits of information in digital code so that the microcomputer can recognize them and process the information received.

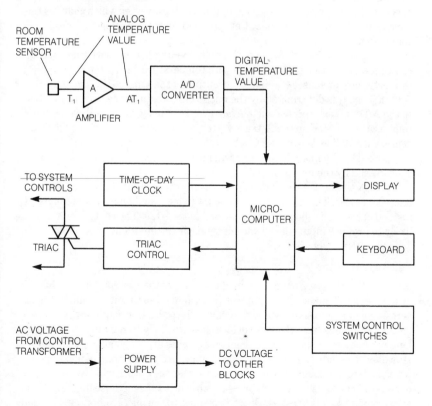

Figure 5-16. *Block Diagram of an Electronic Thermostat*

The microcomputer outputs to the display the digital codes which are converted to decimal digits so that the display can convey to humans the time and temperatures currently programmed into the system. The microcomputer also outputs the digital signals to the TRIAC to turn it ON or OFF. These are digital voltage levels that represent the 0 and 1 logic levels.

Power Supply

All the electronic circuits operate from a dc voltage which is developed by an internal power supply from the 24-volt ac control voltage. Also included inside the power supply are connections to a 9-volt battery which is switched in when main power fails. The battery maintains power on the microcomputer and time-of-day clock circuits so that the information programmed into the electronic thermostat is not lost.

Analog-to-Digital Conversion

Note that the room temperature sensor signal is an analog signal coming from the sensor. It is increased in amplitude by an amplifier with a gain of A and then fed into an analog-to-digital (A/D) converter which changes the analog signal into a digital code. Let's look closer at the analog-to-digital conversion function.

Figure 5-17a shows how the sensor voltage varies with time and shows the calibration of the voltage with temperature. At t_1, the A/D converter circuit senses (samples) the output of the sensor (V_1, in *Figure 5-17a*). Time t_1 is determined by the microcomputer and it sends a timing pulse to the A/D converter as shown in *Figure 5-17b*. Analog voltage V_1 represents a temperature of 51°F so the A/D converter converts it into a digital code that represents 51°F as shown in *Figure 5-17b*. Thus, the digital code 00110011 is recognized by the microcomputer as an input temperature of 51°F and the code is processed by the microcomputer.

A similar type of code appears at the other inputs to the microcomputer. There may be only one bit (which would have a state of 0 or 1) instead of the eight shown in the code of *Figure 5-17b*. The control switches are likely to produce inputs of the one-bit type. Or the input might be a four-bit code from the keyboard keys.

Full System Mode

Now that we have examined the parts of the system, let's see how the system works. The microcomputer is programmed so that it continually scans across the inputs in sequence to determine the codes that might exist on the inputs. The codes from the control switches are likely to remain constant for long periods of time because the control switches are not changed very often. However, the codes from the keyboard inputs are present only when keys are pressed, but the scanning rate is so fast that any key press will always be detected. If no keys have been pressed, no code exists on those inputs. However, if a key is pressed, the code is input to the microcomputer, decoded and identified as to its meaning.

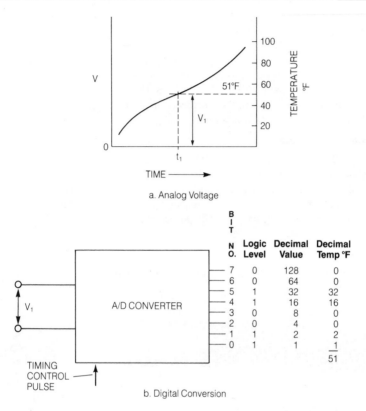

Figure 5-17. *Sensor Voltage Converted to Digital Code*

Suppose the operator requests that the room temperature be displayed by pressing the "TEMP ACTUAL" key. The microcomputer locates the temperature which it stored in its memory the last time it told the A/D converter to sense the output of the room temperature sensor. The information is stored in memory in digital codes that the computer understands so the codes must be converted to decimal numbers that humans understand. The microcomputer performs the conversion and sends the information to the display electronics where the temperature is displayed by the LED as decimal numbers.

The time-of-day electronics is a time-of-day clock. By pressing the "TIME CLOCK" key, the current digital code representing the time of day is decoded by the microcomputer and sent to be displayed. If the time is to be set, an appropriate "TIME am" or "TIME pm" key is pressed, and the desired time is input to the internal electronics by pressing the appropriate number keys for the hour and minutes. The internal clock continues from this set point and keeps the time of day very accurately just as a digital watch does.

All during the time that the operator is pressing the various keys, the microcomputer is controlled by a program stored in memory. The program tells the microcomputer when to scan the inputs, what to do with the inputs it detects, and what outputs to energize to do what the operator has requested. For example, if the keystroke of key number 7 means that the hour digit of the time-of-day clock should be changed to seven, then the microcomputer recognizes this and does it under the direction of its internal program and by the codes it detects on its inputs.

A Specific Example

The system operation and the function of the electronics can be clarified further by a specific example. In this example, the thermostat is controlling the temperature of a home where both mother and father work away from home and the kids are in school during the day. A front panel drawing is shown in *Figure 5-18*. The positions of the control switches are as shown in *Table 5-1*.

Table 5-1. *Control Switch Positions*

SYSTEM—HEAT
FAN—AUTO
MODE—DAY/NIGHT

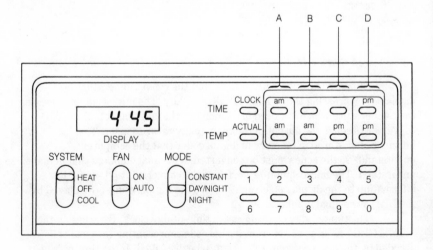

Figure 5-18. *Electronic Thermostat Control Panel*

With the MODE switch in the DAY/NIGHT position, the electronic
thermostat automatically controls the time and temperature settings selected
for the following conditions:

1. When the family arises in the morning.
2. When the family leaves the house for the day.
3. When the family returns to the house in the afternoon.
4. When the family goes to bed.

The time and temperature settings are entered into the microcomputer
memory by the combination of keys that are pressed. Therefore, if the family
normally arises at 6:15 AM, leaves the house by 8:30 AM, returns at 4:00 PM
and retires at 11:00 PM, the times and temperatures programmed into the
system might be as shown in *Table 5-2*. (Temperatures are in °F.)

Table 5-2. *Time and Temperature Schedule*

Condition	Time	Temperature
1	6:00 AM	72
2	8:30 AM	60
3	3:45 PM	72
4	11:00 PM	65

Condition 1 time and temperature are progammed by using the "am"
keys labeled group A in *Figure 5-18*. The "TIME am" key is pressed and then
the number keys of 0600 are pressed to set the hour and minutes. The display
shows the time that was set. The temperature is programmed in a similar
fashion by pressing the "TEMP am" key and the number keys 72. Conditions
2, 3, and 4 times and temperatures are set in a similar manner by using the
group B, C, and D keys, respectively. With all these times and temperatures
entered into its memory, the electronic thermostat adjusts the temperature of
the home up and down according to the programmed schedule.

As the microcomputer scans all of its inputs, it is monitoring the inputs from the room temperature sensor and from the time-of-day clock. The actual time is compared with the programmed set-back times to determine which programmed temperature it should use as its control reference. Then it continually compares the digital code out of the A/D converter representing the actual room temperature with the digital code from memory that represents the reference temperature. If the room temperature is below the reference temperature, the microcomputer turns ON the TRIAC which turns on the heat since the "SYSTEM" switch is set to "HEAT". When the room temperature approaches the reference temperature, a built-in anticipator circuit turns OFF the TRIAC and the heat source, but keeps the blower running. Now you can understand what was meant when it was stated earlier that the decision to turn ON and OFF the TRIAC was not determined only by the room temperature sensor and the reference temperature. As you can see, that decision depends also on the time-of-day codes and by the time and temperature codes stored in the computer memory.

This example has shown the basic functional operation of the system for the DAY/NIGHT mode. The other modes operate similarly. The NIGHT mode has only two time and temperature settings, one for bedtime and one for rising time. The CONSTANT mode continually maintains only one temperature 24 hours a day.

Because the system is electronic and uses a microcomputer, functions other than temperature control are easy to add. For example, a timed lock-out feature which prevents rapid system cycling due to the thermostat "diddling" or momentary power loss saves energy and protects cooling system compressors. Protective features that return the system to a reference temperature of 72°F if all power fails can be added easily.

The example discussed was a heat cycle with set-back temperatures; however, the electronic system can handle equally well a cooling cycle with set-up temperatures. In addition, electronic control systems are available for heat pump systems and evaporative cooling systems.

OTHER ELECTRONIC CONTROL SYSTEMS

The example electronic thermostat discussed above offers operating convenience and versatility to the user. In more complex electronic controllers such as those used for commercial buildings, a central computer offers similar features as well as more precise system control to reduce energy expenditures and improve room environmental conditions. The computer-based controller also can provide printed or displayed outputs which give complete information on room conditions, heating and cooling element conditions, and even continuous evaluation of heat flows and energy costs.

Further, since computer-based controllers are easily reprogrammed, it is possible to change the way in which a system is controlled to try different heating and cooling strategies to determine which strategy offers the best operating conditions and costs. These topics will be taken up later in this book as an illustration of how electronic control techniques can be used to significantly improve system performance and efficiency.

WHAT HAVE WE LEARNED?

1. Some heating systems use electrical energy to produce thermal energy through the use of resistive heating elements or a heat pump. Other heating systems use the chemical energy of coal, oil or gas to produce thermal energy through combustion.

2. Thermal energy is transferred by heat exchangers to a fluid for transportation of the thermal energy to building spaces where it is needed. The fluid may be air, water or a chemical refrigerant depending on the type of system.

3. Cooling is performed by using the principle of the evaporation of a liquid to remove heat from the surrounding air or liquid.

4. Evaporative cooling can take place in a water cooling tower which provides cold water for a chilled water cooling system.

5. Cooling also can be accomplished by an electrically powered refrigeration system using a chemical refrigerant which is circulated through an evaporator coil around which the air or water to be cooled is flowing. The evaporation of the refrigerant in this coil chills the air or water and changes the liquid to a gas. A compressor and condenser coil are required to return the refrigerant to the liquid state for recycling.

6. Control systems are required for both heating and cooling. In the past, bimetallic strip thermostats, solenoid valves, and electromagnetic relays have been used for fuel control and fluid control.

7. Modern systems use electronic solid-state temperature sensors, solid-state switches and solid-state microcomputers that provide increased reliability, better control, more versatility, and more convenience. As a result, energy use and cost can be reduced while providing a better quality environment.

Quiz for Chapter 5

1. Heating and cooling systems primarily use what type of heat transfer?
   a. convection
   b. radiation
   c. conduction
   d. all of the above

2. A heat exchanger is necessary in combustion furnaces because the:
   a. duct air flow could extinguish the fire.
   b. heat exchanger is more efficient than blowing the hot combustion air directly into the room.
   c. heat exchanger keeps harmful combustion products out of the room air.

3. In a gas-fired furnace, the blower motor can be turned on if the:
   a. room thermostat indicates the need for heat.
   b. pilot thermocouple indicates the presence of a pilot light.
   c. duct temperature thermostat is indicating a high enough temperature.
   d. all of the above.

4. The heat pump operates by:
   a. performing work on a heat transport fluid.
   b. transporting heat from a resistance heater to another location.
   c. circulating a hot (or cold) fluid from one location to another.

5. The anticipator in a thermostat assembly is used to:
   a. cause the furnace to be turned on before heat is actually needed.
   b. avoid burning the furnace any longer than necessary to cause the room temperature to reach its target value.
   c. turn the blower motor on at the appropriate time.
   d. turn the blower motor off before the furnace turns off.

6. If a liquid condenses on a conductive surface, the temperature of that surface will:
   a. rise.
   b. fall.
   c. remain the same.

7. In a cooling system, a condensate drain below the heat exchanger:
   a. collects water that condenses out of the duct air.
   b. collects water that is condensed from the refrigerant.
   c. provides a water cooled surface to cool the duct air.
   d. is used in conjunction with the condenser coil for cooling.

8. In a chilled water system, the tower blower motor will be energized if the:
   a. room thermostat indicates the need to cool room air.
   b. water reservoir is low.
   c. water reservoir temperature is too low.
   d. water reservoir temperature is too high.

9. In a refrigeration (heat pump) system, the purpose of the compressor is to:
   a. convert the refrigerant to vapor form at a high pressure.
   b. convert the refrigerant to liquid form.
   c. cool the liquid refrigerant.
   d. cause the refrigerant to evaporate and give up its heat.

10. The advantage of an electronic thermostat over a conventional thermostat is that it:
    a. offers more operational convenience.
    b. provides more precise temperature and time settings.
    c. allows more set-back combinations.
    d. provides better control of the heating and cooling system.
    e. all of the above.

How to Control Solar Energy

ABOUT THIS CHAPTER

A great amount of the energy available on earth comes from or has come from the sun. The amount of energy reaching the earth's surface every day from the sun is far greater than the energy needs of man for the foreseeable future. The key to using this vast source of energy is developing cost effective methods for collecting and storing the energy. Once the energy has been collected and stored, it can be used as needed. This chapter explains how electronic control systems can be utilized to increase the efficiency of these collecting and storing processes as well as to make the use of solar energy compatible with the use of conventional energy sources.

HOW MUCH SOLAR ENERGY IS AVAILABLE?

The amount of solar energy reaching the earth's outer atmosphere is enormous. In fact, the amount of energy is so large, that if all of it were to reach the earth's surface, much of life as we now know it could not exist. Absorption and reflection of the solar radiation by the earth's atmosphere reduces the amount and types of radiation that reaches the earth's surface to an acceptable level as shown in *Figure 6-1*.

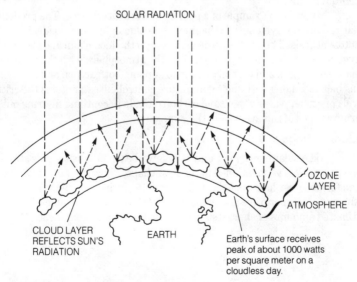

Figure 6-1. Solar Energy

Filtering by Earth's Atmosphere

The earth's atmosphere consists of a thick layer of nitrogen and oxygen surrounded by a relatively thin layer of ozone. When the sun's radiation hits the outer layers of the atmosphere, about 25 to 30% of the energy is absorbed by the ozone, water vapor, and carbon dioxide in the various layers of the earth's atmosphere. Thus, on a clear day without clouds, about 70 to 75% of the solar radiation that hits the upper atmosphere reaches the earth's surface. Clouds reflect solar radiation so the surface area and thickness of the cloud cover greatly affect the amount of energy that reaches the earth, but the average amount is still a very large amount of energy.

The total is 300 trillion (3 followed by 14 zeros) megawatt-hours that reach the earth's surface per year. (A megawatt is one million watts.) This is about the same amount of energy as in a trillion tons of coal. On a daily basis, the energy falling on a square meter of surface area in the U.S.A. peaks at about 1,000 watts (one kilowatt). Of course, this radiation level varies with the time of day, the cloud layer and the location of the point on the earth's surface receiving the radiation.

The solar energy received has a range of frequencies or wavelengths from the lower frequencies (longer wavelengths) of infrared (which heat the earth) through visible light to the very dangerous higher frequencies (shorter wavelengths) of ultraviolet. The harmful ultraviolet is reduced to relatively harmless levels by the ozone layer of the atmosphere, while the very useful lower frequency radiation is reduced somewhat by the ozone, carbon dioxide and water vapor. The result is a well-controlled environment for maintaining life.

Here is an example of a portion of the control cycle. The predominant solar radiation wavelength is that of visible blue light which is ideal for plant photosynthesis. The photosynthesis, through the food chain and the resulting oxygen-carbon dioxide cycle, maintains the atmosphere with the proper balance of oxygen and carbon dioxide to support both animal and plant life. This balance, along with the temperature control, also maintains the critical levels of ozone, water vapor, and carbon dioxide to continue filtering out the harmful types of radiation from the sun.

Natural Storage of Solar Energy

The solar energy not only is received each day, but also is stored as time passes. We've mentioned in the first chapter how the fossil fuels have been formed over long periods of time from the remains of plant life under the influence of temperature and pressure. *Table 6-1* contains some of the estimated amounts of energy stored in fossil fuels and ocean heat.

Table 6-1. *Stored Solar Energy*

Storage Medium	Energy Stored (KWH)
All Oceans	146 times yearly energy received
Gulf of Mexico and Caribbean Sea	180×10^{12}
Fossil Fuel	$60,000 \times 10^{12}$

Source: D.S. Halacy, Jr., *Solar Energy Technology Handbook*, Marcel Dekker, Inc., 1980.

Besides the above, solar energy radiation also produces wind currents, which are estimated to have a potential for 20×10^9 kilowatt-hours (KWH) of energy. Even though all of these amounts of energy stagger the imagination, less than one percent of the total solar energy received on the earth's surface end up as wind, ocean, and fossil fuel energy. The remaining 99% heats the earth's surface. It is this thermal energy that may provide significant portions of humanity's thermal and electrical energy requirements in the future.

HOW CAN SOLAR ENERGY BE USED?

The basic method for using solar energy is to provide a system that can collect and store the energy as shown in *Figure 6-2*. The collector converts the solar radiation into electrical energy, or into energy stored in chemical compounds, or into the thermal energy of a fluid. The type of energy conversion desired determines the type of collector required. Storage is necessary in order to have energy when the sun is not shining.

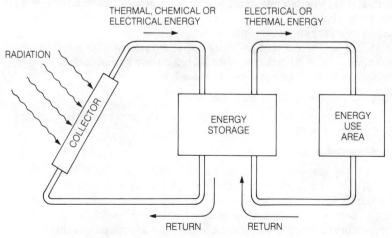

Figure 6-2. *Basic Solar Energy System*

Stored Electrical Energy

Solar cells can collect and convert solar energy to electrical energy. If all of the electrical energy is not used immediately, it can be stored in rechargeable batteries or delivered to an electric power company's transmission system. In the latter case, the "storage" is obtained by selling the energy to the power company to gain energy credits which can be redeemed later for energy for use when solar generation is low.

Stored Chemical Bonds

The electrical energy also may be stored in the form of chemical bonds. If so, the chemical is stored in suitable containers until the time comes to release the energy by conversion, either into electrical energy or into thermal energy through chemical reactions or combustion. Many chemical reactions have been proposed for the conversion. One approach is to have the electrical energy produce oxygen and hydrogen through the hydrolysis of water. The oxygen and hydrogen are stored in separate containers until energy is needed. At that time, they can be recombined to produce heat (thermal energy) through the burning of hydrogen in oxygen. Alternatively, and possibly safer, they can be used in a hydrogen-oxygen fuel cell for generation of electricity which can in turn be used to produce mechanical, light, or thermal energy as needed.

Stored Thermal Energy

The simplest collector is one which collects the thermal energy from solar radiation and transfers it to a fluid. The fluid then is transported to where it is used or stored for future use. The heat in the fluid must be stored in a material that has a high capacity for holding thermal energy. Any given material has a certain capacity for storing heat, but the material used to store thermal energy for later use must be able to retain a relatively large amount of heat for a relatively long time to be able to supply energy during periods of little or no solar energy collection.

All of these techniques of collecting and storing solar energy have advantages and disadvantages, and each has its own special control requirements. Let's look at some of the basic techniques.

HOW DO THERMAL COLLECTORS WORK?

Three general types of solar thermal collectors presently in use are the flat plate, the focusing, and the solar pond.

Flat Plate Collector

The simplest and least expensive collector for small installations is the flat plate, non-focusing collector. This type of collector heats air or water to about 25° to 60°C for use in heating buildings or for providing a hot water supply. Some special types of flat plate collectors can provide fluid temperatures above 100°C, but these are for special applications that can afford the more expensive collectors.

The basic structure of a flat plate, non-focusing collector is shown in *Figure 6-3* for two cases. The collector structure of *Figure 6-3a* is used for directly heating air, while the structure of *Figure 6-3b* is used for heating a liquid.

Collectors can be built in different ways, but they all share some common features and are designed to be as efficient as possible. The efficiency is increased by using dead air spaces and insulating material to reduce losses due to convection and conduction. They all have an absorber plate that is designed so it doesn't reflect very much of the radiation striking the absorber plate. They all have a transparent cover to permit the radiation to pass through to the absorber plate and to trap a hot air layer above the absorber plate to reduce heat loss by conduction. They have a layer of insulating material to prevent heat loss by conduction from the hot air or liquid.

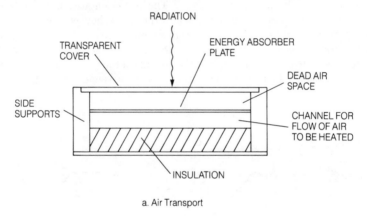

a. Air Transport

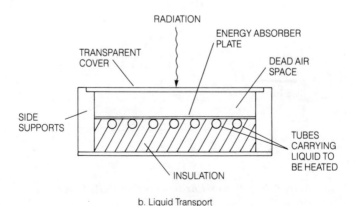

b. Liquid Transport

Figure 6-3. *Structures of Flat Plate Collectors*

As a result of getting hot due to absorbing the solar radiation, the absorber plate transfers heat to either the air flowing across the other side of the absorber plate or to a liquid flowing through tubes bonded to the absorber. The slower the fluid moves through the collector, or the greater the path length of the fluid through the collector, the hotter the fluid gets before it leaves the collector. Most thermal collectors use clear glass for the transparent cover and flat black paint on the absorber plate. More expensive designs may use two glass plates sealed to trap a dead air space or a vacuum between them to further reduce convective and conductive loss. Inexpensive collectors use a transparent plastic cover, though such covers often discolor and deteriorate with time because of the high temperature and exposure to ultraviolet radiation.

Since flat plate collectors are non-focusing, they must be oriented toward the sun for maximum efficiency. The best orientation is when the sun's rays are exactly perpendicular to the absorber plate; however, some compromise must be made for collectors mounted in a fixed position. As shown in *Figure 6-4*, such collectors are set so that they are facing south and are tilted with respect to earth at an angle of the latitude of the location plus 15 degrees. This tilt has been found to be the optimum for year-round solar collection for most regions.

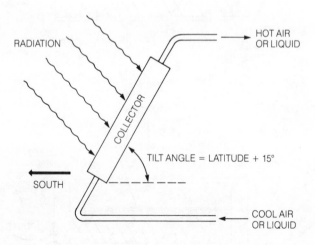

Figure 6-4. *Optimum Position for Flat Plate Collectors*

Focusing Collector

Higher fluid temperatures can be obtained with a smaller surface area if a focusing type of collector is used instead of the flat plate collector. The focusing collector causes the sun rays to be focused on the fluid container to be heated. The increased heating effect of focusing the sun's rays is well known to anyone who has burned holes in paper using a magnifying glass to concentrate the rays. Similarly, by concentrating the rays onto a fluid container with either lenses or mirrors, fluid temperatures above 300°C can be produced. If the fluid is water, this temperature is high enough to produce a low grade steam which can be used to drive a steam turbine. The turbine then can be used to drive a compressor in a refrigeration system or to drive an electrical generator for electrical energy output. Many industrial processes also use such low grade steam.

A proposed design for a focusing collector using a spherical mirror is shown in *Figure 6-5*. If the rays striking such a mirror are traced for various positions of the sun with respect to the mirror, one finds that the rays strike the absorber cylinder if the cylinder is on the solar axis; that is, it is on a line to the sun's position in the sky. In this example, the mirror is stationary, but the absorber must be continually aligned with the sun's position. Thus, a sun tracking control system must be built. It may be a relatively inexpensive system since only the low mass of the absorber cylinder must be moved.

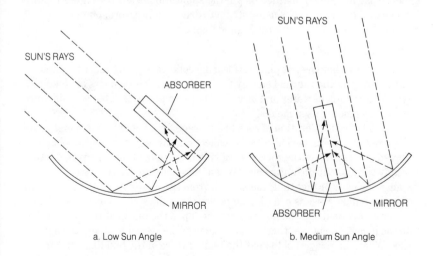

a. Low Sun Angle

b. Medium Sun Angle

Figure 6-5. Focusing Solar Collector

One way to avoid the expense of a tracking system altogether is to use a stationary focusing collector and stationary absorber. An example of this type of collector is the compound parabolic concentrator (CPC) shown in *Figure 6-6*. All of the radiation incident within the cone shown hits the absorber. As long as the sun's radiation is maintained within this cone, the collector does not have to be repositioned. Only if rays (such as those from diffusing effects such as clouds) come from outside the cone will they be reflected back out into the atmosphere.

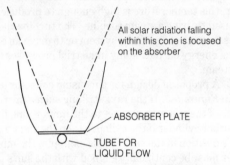

Figure 6-6. Compound Parabolic Concentrator Solar Collector

The CPC, the spherical mirror and other concentrating or focusing collectors are more expensive than flat plate collectors and their added expense usually can be justified only if the application needs the higher fluid temperatures. Applications using steam to drive compressors, pumps or electrical generators require the higher temperatures.

Storage of Thermal Energy

For either the flat plate or focusing collectors, there must be some means of storing the thermal energy for use during evening hours or cloudy days. A large tank of water or a large bed of rocks in an insulated container are the most commonly used means.

The basic operation of rock bed storage for a hot air system is shown in *Figure 6-7*. During periods of solar collection, the hot air from the collectors is forced into the top of the rock pile causing them to heat up to a given depth, possibly throughout the entire pile. When the solar radiation decreases because of clouds or nightfall, the air flow from the solar collector is turned off. When the building needs heat during periods that the solar collector is off, the air flow is reversed and the hot rocks at the top of the pile heat the air flowing into the house. Of course, this removes some of the stored heat and cools the rocks. When the rocks cool to near the temperature of the building, the air flow through the rocks is stopped and a standard furnace is turned on to heat the building. Thus, the solar system provides supplemental heating to reduce the amount of electricity or gas used in the conventional part of the heating system. Since the rock storage can be very dusty, a filter must be placed between the rooms receiving heat and the rock storage bin.

Other storage techniques use large pools of water to store the thermal energy. Such pools could be swimming pools with insulated covers (during the winter). In fact, one application of solar heaters is to heat swimming pools for an extended swimming season.

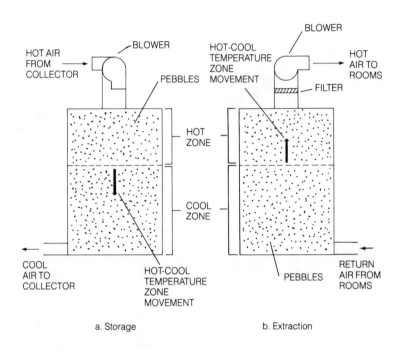

a. Storage   b. Extraction

Figure 6-7. *Heat Storage in Rocks*

Solar Pond

The solar pond technique for solar collection is similar in principle to the flat plate collector except that a pond of salt water is used to collect the sun's energy. A solar pond has the advantages of producing and storing thermal energy in large quantities for both immediate and future use. Also, since relatively inexpensive materials are used, the solar pond may be the lowest cost method to produce large area collectors.

In the solar pond of *Figure 6-8*, the pool of salt water is about one to two meters deep. The salt solution concentration varies with depth and is maintained to provide a non-convective layer. This layer prevents the hot water from rising to the surface and cooling by evaporation and conduction. If this layer is truly non-convective, and if the salt water solution is clear enough to allow a large percentage of the solar radiation to reach the bottom layer in the pond, this bottom layer can get very hot, in the 60 to 80°C range. The heat is extracted from the pond by pipes that run in the bottom layer. The chief advantage of the solar pond over a large surface area flat plate collector is that the pond can be made from very inexpensive materials and with very low installation cost.

All of the thermal collector techniques involve the collection and storage of thermal energy directly from solar radiation. However, the use of solar energy is more versatile when it is converted to electrical energy or the solar energy is stored in chemical bonds. Let's look at these techniques.

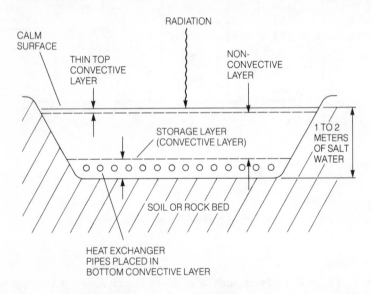

Figure 6-8. Non-Convective Salt Solution Solar Pond

HOW CAN SOLAR ENERGY BE CONVERTED TO ELECTRICAL ENERGY?

Electrical energy can be generated from solar energy by driving an electrical generator with the wind or with a steam turbine or by the direct conversion from solar radiation to electricity with the use of semiconductor diodes that respond to light.

Wind Turbine

The conversion of wind energy to electrical energy has been used for many years to provide electrical power at rural and remote locations. A modern version of this type of electrical power generation plant is shown in *Figure 6-9*. A propeller driven generator is mounted on a tower and is oriented to the direction of wind flow. This type of installation is effective in areas that have winds that are consistently in the 15 to 20 mile per hour range. The propellers range from the two vane models of *Figure 6-9*, to giant four vane models like the Dutch windmills. Propeller diameters range from five or six feet for small power plants to up to 200 feet for large generators. Power outputs per tower range from a few hundred watts to over 2 megawatts.

Since wind energy, like direct solar enegy, is intermittent, some form of energy storage and/or a supplemental energy source must be available for use during periods of low wind velocity. Small rural installations use banks of batteries to provide electrical energy storage at considerable expense. Large installations use the wind generated electricity only as a supplement to a conventional electrical power plant to reduce overall energy costs. In these installations, energy storage usually is not used.

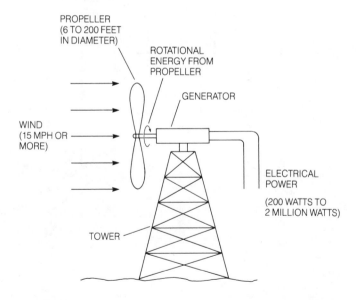

Figure 6-9. *Wind Energy Conversion*

Heliostat Concentrator and Steam Turbine

As mentioned earlier, solar energy can be concentrated by certain types of collectors to provide low temperature steam. Such steam can be used to drive a steam turbine which in turn drives an electrical generator. An example of a large power generator in the 10 megawatt range is shown in *Figure 6-10*. This is basically a large mirror made from thousands of individually mounted and controlled mirrors called heliostats. The control system aligns each mirror to reflect the solar energy striking it to the absorber on the boiler surface. The result is a large amount of radiation directed to and absorbed by the boiler to produce steam with temperatures in excess of 500°C. Some of the high temperature steam can be stored in a well-insulated liquid or solid material with a high heat capacity for use later during heavy cloud cover periods or at night. Thus, part of the steam generated in the boiler is used directly to drive the steam turbines of the electrical power plant and the rest is stored in a large thermal reservoir for later use.

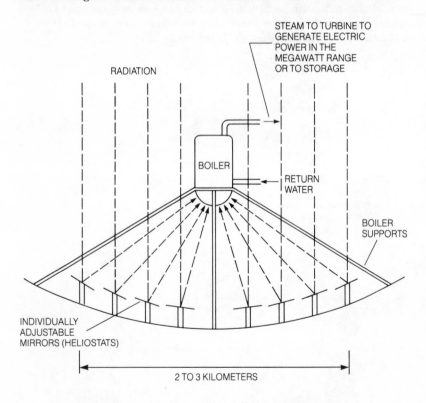

Figure 6-10. *Large Power Generation Solar Collector*

Solar Cell

A more direct conversion of solar energy into electricity is through the use of semiconductor light sensitive (photovoltaic) diode converters, commonly called solar cells. These were discussed in Chapter 2, but the basic features of their operation is presented again in *Figure 6-11* for review.

The silicon on one side of a p-n semiconductor junction has been doped with a type of impurity to cause a lack of electrons in the material. These voids in the electronic structure are called holes. This material is called p-type. The silicon on the other side of the junction has been doped with a different type of impurity to cause a large number of free electrons to be available on that side of the junction. This material is called n-type.

By shining solar radiation on the surface of the p material, electron-hole pairs are generated—electrons which are negatively charged and holes which are positively charged. The electrons move away from the point of generation toward the n region. Once they reach the n region, they can flow easily through the n region, through the external load resistor and back to the p material. At this point, each electron recombines with a positively charged hole to produce a bound electron (one that is not free to move). Then the solar radiation again breaks the electron free, producing another hole and electron pair, and the flow process repeats.

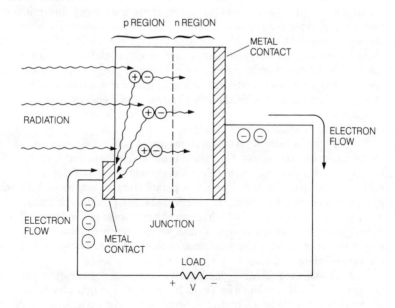

Figure 6-11. *Solar Cell Operation*

The number of electrons produced by this process, thus, the amount of current flow through the external load, depends on the surface area of the diode, the amount or intensity of solar radiation, and the properties of the diode and junction. The voltage produced by the diode is in the 0.5 to 0.7 volt range at no current flow and about two-thirds of this value for maximum power output.

The power output provided by each diode is in the range of 100 watts per square meter of surface area. This can be expressed in terms of a conversion efficiency, which varies from 1% for a poor quality cell up to 18% for a very high quality cell. If the solar radiation incident on the cell contains 1,000 watts of energy per square meter, a 10% efficient cell will provide an output of 100 watts for each square meter of solar cell surface area. Since each solar cell has a relatively small area, a very large number of cells are required to produce even a moderate amount of power. Of course, the number of cells required increases rapidly as the cell efficiency decreases. Thus, the key to making economical power plants in the 10 kilowatt range or less using solar cells is to have low cost, high efficiency cells available. Even with such cells, some means of storing the electrical energy for use during dark periods is required.

STORAGE OF ELECTRICAL ENERGY

The electrical energy produced by solar cell arrays is either stored in rechargeable batteries or some other form of chemical energy. Batteries are very expensive for even medium (less than 10 kilowatts) power facilities and are not considered to be practical for most applications. In fact, if there were a large number of solar electrical plants, there would not be enough raw materials available to make the number of batteries needed. As a result, much research has been concentrated on finding a method to store the electrical energy in chemical form which can then release stored energy as electricity through the use of fuel cells, or the stored energy can be converted to thermal energy through combustion reactions.

There have been several systems proposed for the storage of electrical energy in this way. One common method is to convert water to hydrogen and oxygen by passing electrical current through water, and collecting the hydrogen and oxygen in separate storage containers. When the hydrogen is burned in oxygen, the chemical reaction produces thermal energy and water. Alternatively, the hydrogen and oxygen can be used in a fuel cell to directly provide electrical energy. (The hydrogen-oxygen fuel cell was discussed in Chapter 2.) The problem with this particular system is that it is not very efficient.

A safe and potentially inexpensive storage and generation system has been proposed and developed by Texas Instruments Incorporated to use the electrolysis of the chemical, hydrogen bromide, to produce hydrogen and bromine. These can be stored readily and then recombined in a hydrogen bromide fuel cell to produce electricity.

Hydrogen Bromide Solar Converter

The hydrogen bromide (HBr) electrolysis has an important advantage over the electrolysis of other chemical compounds; that is, it occurs at around 1 volt of potential. This coincides with the output voltage of two high quality silicon solar cells placed in series. The circuit and structure of this type of conversion is shown in *Figure 6-12*.

In the simplified circuit diagram of *Figure 6-12a*, the two photovoltaic diodes (solar cells) in series produce electron flow with a generated potential of about 1 volt. The electrons at the hydrogen electrode combine with hydrogen ions (H^+) to produce hydrogen gas (H_2) which is sent to a storage cannister. Corresponding to this action, at the other electrode two bromine ions (Br^-) each give up an electron for flow through the diode circuit, producing bromine (Br_2). The bromine remains dissolved in some hydrogen bromide (HBr) and the solution is then pumped to the bromine storage tank.

In an actual converter structure, as shown in *Figure 6-12b*, the diodes and the container for the hydrogen bromide solution are all one integral structure, with the hydrogen producing cells separated from the bromine producing cells. This allows the hydrogen and bromine produced by the combination solar cell conversion and electrolysis to be collected and sent to their respective storage containers. The solar radiation is admitted through the glass cover plate and is reflected into the p and n regions of the series solar cell diodes to generate the hole-electron pairs that produce the electron flows and potential difference that produce the electrolysis as described above.

The hydrogen is stored in a cooled hydride storage cannister filled with a calcium-nickel alloy that absorbs and holds the hydrogen until it is released as needed through a low temperature heating process. The bromine, which contains the heat of reaction of the electrolysis conversion, is stored in a tank which is designed as a heat exchanger. This thermal energy is a by-product and can be used to heat the building that houses the system and provides the heat required to release the hydrogen from the hydride storage cannister.

Hydrogen Bromide Fuel Cell

While the heat from the bromine tank heat exchanger is useful thermal energy, the main energy from the system is produced from the fuel cell which recombines the hydrogen and bromine to produce electricity as needed. The resulting hydrogen bromide is returned to the hydrogen bromide solar converter for re-use.

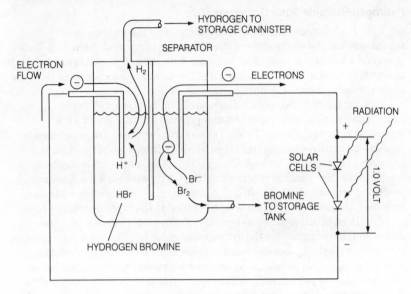

a. Circuit of Electrochemical Converter

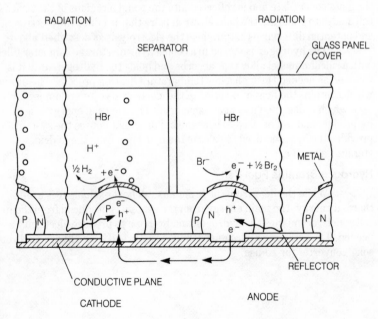

b. Converter Structure

Figure 6-12. *Solar Electrochemical Conversion*

The basic operation of the fuel cell is shown in *Figure 6-13*. It is similar to the hydrogen-oxygen fuel cell discussed in Chapter 2. The hydrogen (H_2) is input at the hydrogen electrode where it is separated into a hydrogen ion (H^+) and an electron (e^-). The electron flows through the external load resistor and the hydrogen ion moves through the ion exchange membrane over to the bromine electrode. At the bromine electrode, the hydrogen ion (H^+) combines with the bromine atom (Br_2) and the electron from the external circuit to produce hydrogen bromide (HBr). The load in the circuit of *Figure 6-13* represents the motors, heaters, and lights that may require electrical power.

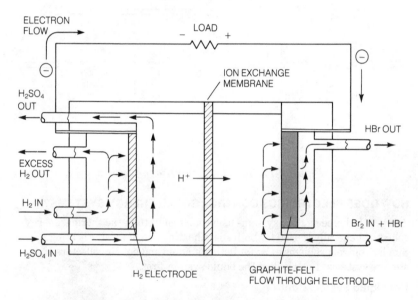

Figure 6-13. *Cross-Section of a Hydrogen Bromide Fuel Cell*

Overall System

The basic block diagram of the overall system is shown in *Figure 6-14*. This system generates and stores chemical energy during the daylight hours for ready re-generation of electrical energy when needed. Some alternative systems use the solar energy both to generate electricity directly for immediate use and for chemical storage for later use. However, the general principles of chemical storage and re-generation of electrical power through the use of fuel cells is similar in all such systems. One interesting sidelight is that such solar systems could feed energy to the power companies during periods of peak production and receive energy credit for energy used from the power company during times when the solar system cannot meet the required load.

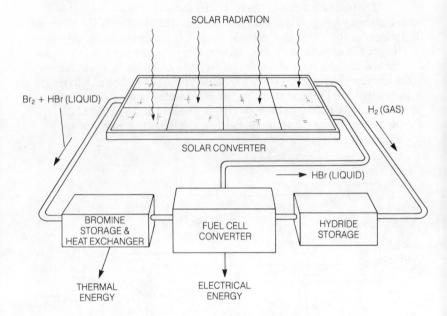

Figure 6-14. *Complete Solar Energy System*

HOW DOES ELECTRONICS CONTROL SOLAR ENERGY SYSTEMS?

In home heating systems using solar collectors, the thermal energy collected generally is used for both space heating and hot water heating. Similar control problems exist for both hot liquid and hot air collectors and storage systems. Let's look at the liquid system first.

Hot Liquid System Control

The overall system is illustrated in *Figure 6-15*. The solar collectors are of the flat-plate liquid type. The liquid is non-corrosive and non-freezing such as a mixture of ethylene glycol and water much like an automobile coolant. As solar energy heats the liquid in the collector tubes, the control system monitors the temperature of the liquid in the storage tank and the temperature of the liquid in the solar collectors. If the storage tank liquid temperature is lower (within some predetermined limit) than the collector temperature, the control system turns on the solar collector pump to pump hot liquid through the storage tank (or through a heat exchanger in the storage tank). When the storage tank liquid temperature becomes as hot as the collector liquid temperature (within the predetermined limit), the pump is turned off. Heat to the household hot water supply and to the air flow in the air ducts is then taken from the storage tank as needed by the control system turning on the respective pumps.

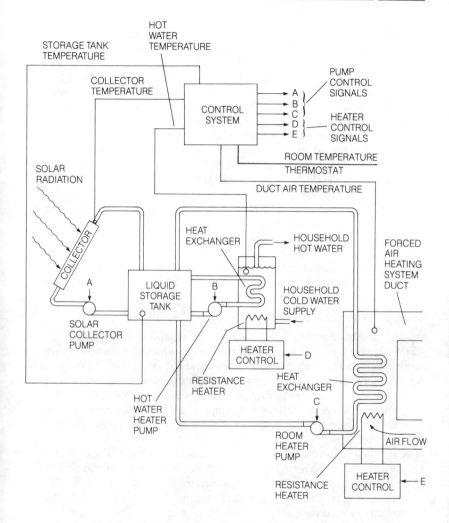

Figure 6-15. Control of Hot Liquid Solar System

Hot Water and Room Heat Control

The hot water heater and room air heating control provides for heat to be delivered either from the solar storage tank, from a conventional gas or electrical heating element, or from both, depending on the amount of heat stored in the tank. The control strategy is similar to the control of the solar collector pump discussed above. In fact, the hot water heater control is almost identical to the storage tank control.

If the temperature sensor in the hot water heater indicates a water temperature below that desired, heat must be supplied to the water in the hot water tank. First, the control system checks the temperature of the solar storage tank liquid. If it is above a minimum level, the pump that circulates fluid between the storage tank and the heat exchanger in the hot water heater is turned on. This pumping continues until the hot water heater water reaches the desired temperature or until the temperature in the storage tank falls too low to supply heat for the hot water heater. For the latter condition, the electrical resistance heater (or gas burner) is turned on and the pump to the storage tank is turned off. If, when the heating period first begins, the temperature in the storage tank is too low, the pump to the storage tank is never turned on and the hot water heater just works as a conventional water heater using electrical resistance heating (or a gas burner).

The control of the room air heating works in a similar fashion except that the room thermostat is used as the temperature sensor to decide if heat is needed. Again, heat will be provided from the storage tank by turning on the room heater pump to provide hot fluid to the heat exchanger in the air duct if the storage tank temperature is high enough. Otherwise, a conventional furnace electrical resistance heater or gas burner is turned on to provide the room air heat.

Electronic Control System

The basic electronic control subsystem is shown in block diagram form in *Figure 6-16*. The two temperature sensors measure the heat source temperature and the heat destination temperature. If the control subsystem is for the solar collector pump, the source temperature is the fluid temperature in the collector and the destination temperature is the storage tank liquid temperature. Similarly, if the source temperature is the fluid in the storage tank and the destination temperature is either the room air temperature or the hot water temperature, the control subsystem is used to control the pump between the storage tank and the respective heat exchanger. The temperature sensor outputs are converted to useful voltages by the electronic amplifiers. The outputs of these amplifiers are sent to a circuit that subtracts the destination temperature voltage from the source temperature voltage. This voltage difference is compared to a reference value by two comparator amplifiers. One comparator determines if the difference is great enough to justify turning on the pump motor while the other determines if the difference is too small to justify turning on the pump. The outputs of these comparators control the on-off state of the pump motor through a relay or electronic switch. The electronic switch would have the necessary logic and TRIAC elements for the motor control (Chapter 4).

The control system shown in *Figure 6-16* is an all analog function system, but the control system also could be realized with digital electronic devices. In a digital control system, the outputs of temperature sensors would be inputs to A/D converters and would be converted to digital codes. The digital codes would be sent to an ALU and a subtraction would produce the difference code. Digital comparators would compare the difference code with the high and low reference values and they in turn would output a digital signal to turn on or off a control memory element (a flip-flop) that in turn would control the on-off state of the motor through a solid-state switch or a relay.

It is easy to visualize how a computerized digital control system also could be used. Now the individual control subsystems are replaced with one computer control system that samples each of the control loops many times a second to determine what control action is needed. This system would have the advantage of controlling both the solar and conventional parts of the heating system, and could optimize the temperature difference limits used to determine the on or off state of any given pump motor. Let's now look at the hot air system.

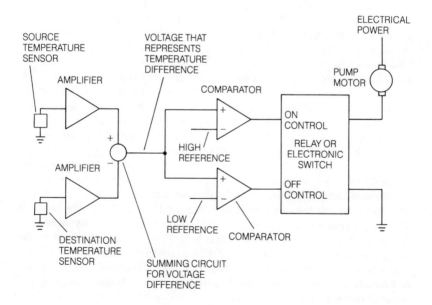

Figure 6-16. *Basic Electronic Control System for Thermal Solar Energy System*

Hot Air System Control

The control of hot air systems can be handled in a manner similar to the control of hot liquid systems. However, there are some additional options available in a hot air collector system as shown in *Figure 6-17*. If room heating is not needed during the daylight hours, the hot air heats the rocks in the rock storage bin to store the heat. When room heating is required during daylight periods, the air flow from the collector is diverted from the rock storage bin to the fan duct for delivery to the rooms requiring heat. During evening hours or hours of low solar collection, heat is delivered to the rooms from the rock storage through the fan duct of the normal heating system. If there is not enough heat in the rock bin, the conventional heating system is turned on.

Each of these situations requires several control elements and sensors. When heat is delivered directly from the collector to the rock bin for storage, the solar collector blower must be on and the duct paths must be set up as shown in *Figure 6-17a*. This configuration blocks air flow between the collector and the rooms and allows air flow between the collector and rock bin. The control system sets up the required air flow paths by positioning the dampers within the duct system. Similarly, when heat is to be delivered to the house directly from the collector, the collector blower must be on and the flow must be from the collector outlet through the room ducts and back from the room to the collector inlet, bypassing the storage bin as shown in *Figure 6-17b*. When heat is to be delivered to the house from the storage bin, the furnace blower must be on to force hot air out of the top of the storage bin (the hot zone) into the room and pull the cooler room air back to the bottom of the storage bin for heating, with the paths to the collector blocked as shown in *Figure 6-17c*. When the rocks are too cool to provide heat, the furnace heater and blower are turned on with the dampers positioned as shown in *Figure 6-17a*. In this case, the solar collector blower may be on if there is enough solar radiation to store heat; otherwise it will be off.

All of these control options require the sensing of the collector outlet temperature, the storage bin outlet temperature, and the room temperatures. If a storage bin temperature some distance down from the outlet is monitored, the control system can anticipate when the stored heat is about to be depleted. When this event is sensed, the control system can turn on the conventional furnace so it will be ready to deliver heat before the stored heat is used up. By using this method, continuous heating with no cold drafts is achieved. A control system of the type shown in *Figure 6-16* could be used in such a system or a digital computer system could be used to provide optimum utilization of the available solar energy.

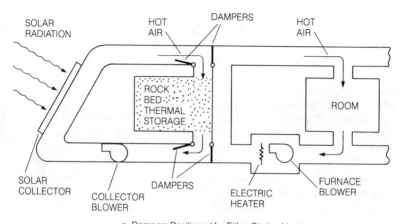

a. Dampers Positioned for Either Storing Heat
from Collector or Heating Rooms from Furnace

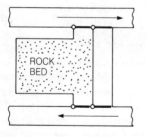

b. Dampers Positioned for Heating Rooms
Directly from Solar Collector

c. Dampers Positioned for Heating Rooms
with Stored Heat

Figure 6-17. *Control of Hot Air Solar System*

Solar Cell Converter Control System

The solar cell converter system requires a more complicated control system than does the thermal solar collector systems. As an example, *Figure 6-18* shows the control system required for an electrochemical solar converter system of the type shown in *Figure 6-14*.

In this type of system (or any system that generates ac electrical power), the generated power must be connected to the house wiring which already is receiving power from the electric power company. This presents a new control situation because the power is an alternating current. To prevent damage to the power generation equipment and household appliances, either the power from the power company must be removed from the lines before the solar generated power is connected, or the solar power must be synchronized both in frequency and phase with the power company's voltage. (When the two are synchronized, the voltage waveforms cross the zero volt point at exactly the same time at all times.) In the latter condition, the power delivered by the power company is supplemented by the solar generated power without any bad effects on either the house appliances or the neighboring power lines.

If the amount of solar power generated is more than the home needs, the excess power flows into the power company's utility lines, which opens the possibility of selling the excess local power to the power company for a further reduction in energy costs. In order to do this, the power company must have a billing structure that allows power sell-back and a metering system must be installed that monitors power flow amounts from the home to the power company as well as power flow from the power company to the home. Experimental systems show this technique to be quite feasible. Even without a sell-back option, the local solar generation of electrical power will significantly reduce the cost of electrical energy from the power company.

Control Functions

The control system of *Figure 6-18* divides into two sections. *Figure 6-18a* is the central control function that establishes the line voltage reference and the phase of the load current in relationship to this reference. A low voltage copy of the power line voltage is provided by the voltage buffer amplifier and a voltage proportional to the load current is provided by the load current buffer amplifier which receives an input from a current transformer sensing the load current in the power line. Both of these inputs are fed to a phase detector which outputs a signal that represents the load current phase. The load current phase and reference voltage signal are then distributed to all fuel cell module controllers like the one of *Figure 6-18b*. The fuel cell control voltage generator establishes a dc fuel cell control voltage that is sent to each fuel cell module. Each fuel cell matches this fuel cell control voltage to determine the amount of the load supplied by each of the fuel cell modules.

In each of the fuel cell module controllers (*Figure 6-18b*), there are two control portions. One portion controls the inverter to set the magnitude and phase of the output voltage as well as how much load is supplied from the respective fuel cell. The other portion controls the bromine supply to the fuel cell.

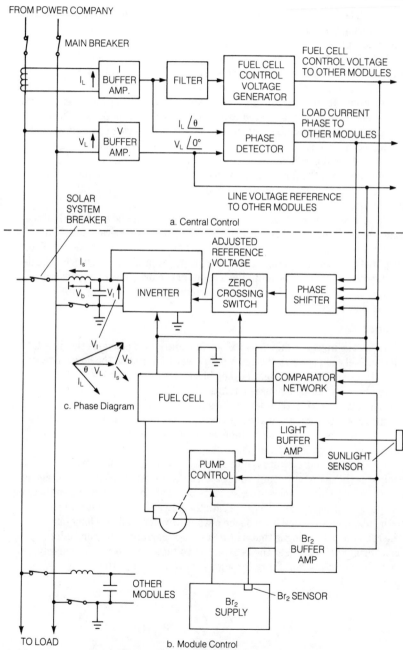

Figure 6-18. Solar Energy System Control

The fuel cell output voltage, the line voltage reference, the voltage representing the load current phase, and the fuel cell control voltage are inputs to a phase shifter whose output is an adjusted reference voltage that is fed to the inverter. The output voltage of the inverter and the adjusted reference voltage are compared to determine the output voltage magnitude, phase and amount of load current supplied. By adjusting the magnitude of the inverter output voltage, the phase diagram of *Figure 6-18c* indicates how the supply current phase is adjusted to match the load current phase. The zero crossing network provides a means of turning the inverter on or off without producing transients (unwanted voltage spikes) on the output voltage.

If the fuel cell voltage goes too low because the fuel cell cannot supply the demand, or if the power demand from the inverter is very small (inverters are inefficient at very low power levels), the comparator turns off the inverter.

The pump control circuit controls the bromine flow rate. When the light sensor detects the presence of enough sunlight to operate the solar converter to charge the system during the day, the pump is turned on. The output of the fuel cell voltage generator, which represents the fuel cell load during discharge, and the amplified output of the bromine level sensor are used by the pump control circuit to determine the required flow rate during discharge.

Inverter

The inverter shown as a block in *Figure 6-18* converts the direct current fuel cell power to the 120 VAC power required on the house power lines. It is shown in more detail in the block diagram of *Figure 6-19*. This particular inverter design uses a relatively high-frequency square wave voltage (up to 20 kHz) that determines the base switching frequency. A gating circuit passes this square wave in bursts to the power switching circuit in a way that will generate an ac voltage waveform of the proper magnitude, current level, frequency, and phase at the output of the inverter.

The gating circuit is controlled by a comparator network that compares the inverter output voltage with the adjusted reference voltage of *Figure 6-18b*. Outputs close to zero volts permit only a short burst so that very few periods of the square wave operate the power switches. Outputs close to the maximum voltage level of the output waveform allow a long burst. The result of the gating is that a large average current flows through the transformer primary near the peak of the voltage waveform. Conversely, a small average current flows through the primary when the voltage is near zero.

These currents are inductively coupled to the secondaries of the transformer. Each of the two secondaries is alternately switched on and off under control of the adjusted reference voltage. The high frequency bursts are rectified to produce one pulse for each burst. The width (duration) of each pulse is determined by the length of the gated burst. This waveform is converted to a smooth and continuous sinusoidal waveform by the LC filter. The buffer inductor in the filter is very important to achieve proper power injection into the power company's transmission system.

This example control system illustrates that an electronic control system may be relatively complex when controlling a solar powered electrical generation system. When the circuitry reaches this level of complexity, the entire control system would probably be built using digital computer control techniques with supporting A/D and D/A converters and power control circuits because of the versatility of digital computer control.

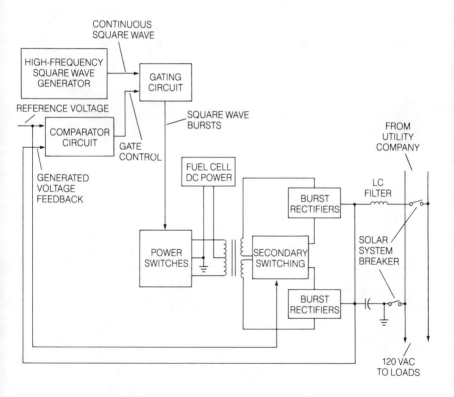

Figure 6-19. *Simplified Inverter Diagram*

WHAT HAVE WE LEARNED?

1. The earth's atmosphere plays a vital part in making sure the right amounts and types of solar energy reach the earth's surface.
2. Tremendous amounts of solar energy reach the earth daily. If this energy could be collected and converted easily and cheaply, it could supply all of our energy needs.
3. Solar energy can be collected directly as thermal energy, or converted directly to electrical energy or indirectly to chemical energy by solar cells.
4. If the solar energy is ultimately converted to electrical power, it must be compatible with the electrical power delivered by the utility company to prevent damage to the utility network, the user appliances, or the solar conversion equipment.
5. Solar systems require some form of energy storage to provide energy during periods without sunshine. The storage can be in the form of thermal energy, electrical energy, or chemical energy.
6. The purpose of a solar energy control system is to extract the maximum thermal or electrical energy from the system for a given configuration of solar collectors and storage techniques.

Quiz for Chapter 6

1. Of the energy that reaches the earth's upper atmosphere each year, what percent is absorbed by the earth's atmosphere?
  a. 5
  b. 10
  c. 30
  d. 50

2. Of the total solar energy reaching earth each year, what percent is available for conversion or direct use by man?
  a. 10
  b. 30
  c. 50
  d. over 90

3. About how many kilowatts per square meter reaches the earth's surface under the best conditions?
  a. 0.5
  b. 1
  c. 2
  d. 1,000

4. What range of frequencies of the incident solar radiation is greatly reduced by the ozone layer in the upper atmosphere?
  a. visible light
  b. ultraviolet radiation
  c. infrared radiation
  d. radio waves

5. The radiation reaching the earth's surface is centered around the:
  a. ultraviolet range.
  b. visible light range.
  c. infrared range.
  d. radio frequency range.

6. The oceans store what portion of the total annual energy received from the sun?
  a. 20%
  b. 50%
  c. 100%
  d. 2 times
  e. over 100 times

7. A flat plate solar collector:
  a. focuses the solar energy onto a receiving tube.
  b. acts much like a greenhouse to trap energy.
  c. is more expensive than a parabolic collector.
  d. converts solar energy into electrical energy.

8. A solar pond:
  a. is a focusing type of solar collector.
  b. converts solar energy into electrical energy.
  c. is essentially a large flat plate collector with built-in thermal storage.
  d. uses air as the heat storage fluid.

9. The least expensive (per square meter) type of collector for large collector installations is the:
  a. flat plate.
  b. parabolic.
  c. cylindrical.
  d. solar pond.

10. The collector that offers the maximum temperature of thermal fluid temperature is the:
  a. parabolic.
  b. flat plate.
  c. solar pond.
  d. photovoltaic cell.

11. Thermal energy can be stored in:
  a. a rock pile through which the hot air from the collector is passed.
  b. a large pool of water.
  c. batteries.
  d. any of the above.
  e. a and b above.

12. Large electrical solar power generating plants use:
  a. photovoltaic cells.
  b. separation of fuel elements through hydrolysis and later burning of these to produce steam.
  c. generation of steam by focusing solar energy from a large mirror field into a boiler.
  d. wind turbines.

13. Electrical power systems for use in outer space use solar power to generate electricity by:
   a. photovoltaic cells.
   b. separation of fuel elements through hydrolysis and later burning of these to produce steam.
   c. generation of steam by focusing solar energy from a large mirror field onto a boiler.
   d. wind turbines.

14. For each square meter, photovoltaic diodes produces a power level in the range of:
   a. 1 microwatt.
   b. 10 milliwatts.
   c. 100 watts.
   d. 1000 kilowatts.

15. Each photovoltaic diode produces its maximum power at around ___ volts?
   a. 0.2
   b. 0.5
   c. 1.0
   d. 1.5

16. A hydrogen bromide converter (or other hydrolysis converter) uses what device to produce electricity?
   a. photovoltaic converter
   b. steam generation from solar thermal energy
   c. steam generation from combustion of hydrogen and bromine
   d. fuel cell

17. In a converter of the type of problem 16, energy is stored in:
   a. rock beds.
   b. batteries.
   c. chemical components.
   d. inertia.

18. In the hydrogen bromide converter, hydrogen is stored as:
   a. a gas in a pressurized container.
   b. a hydride.
   c. part of a water molecule.
   d. a liquid.

19. In a thermal solar system, the electronic control system controls:
   a. when the solar collection is sufficient to provide heating and thermal storage.
   b. whether present solar collection is to be used for heating or storage of energy.
   c. whether the conventional heating or solar heating is to be used for heating water and rooms.
   d. the operation of the duct blowers, conventional heating elements, and the solar heating components.
   e. all of the above.

20. In a photovoltaic converter, the inverter is used:
   a. to convert electrical energy back into thermal energy.
   b. to determine when hydrogen and bromine levels are adequate to generate needed electrical power.
   c. to determine when the fluid pumps of the system are turned on and to control their operation.
   d. to convert the dc voltage from the hydrogen bromide converter into ac power for connection to the house power lines.

7

Controlling Internal Combustion Engines

ABOUT THIS CHAPTER

One of the chief uses of energy is for transportation. It may be the transportation of goods or it may be the transportation of people. Private automobiles, buses, trucks and trains use either the gasoline or diesel fueled internal combustion engine. As in all systems, one must understand how the system works before the control of such a system can be achieved. Therefore, the basic operation of the internal combustion engine will be covered first in this chapter along with a description of the important control variables in this type engine. Then, the discussion will show how electronics can control these variables.

WHAT IS AN INTERNAL COMBUSTION ENGINE?

In the internal combustion engine, an air-fuel mixture is introduced into a closed cylinder in which it is compressed by a piston and then ignited. The combustion (burning) of the fuel causes a rapid rise in the cylinder pressure which is converted to useful mechanical energy by the piston and crankshaft which is connected to an external load.

The Spark-Ignited Gasoline Engine

The four strokes of a four-stroke-per-cycle, spark-ignited, gasoline engine are shown in *Figure 7-1*.

At the beginning of the intake stroke *(Figure 7-1a)*, the intake valve opens and the piston moves from the top of the cylinder, called top dead center (TDC), to the bottom of the cylinder, called bottom dead center (BDC). The vacuum caused by the piston moving from TDC to BDC pulls the air-fuel mixture from the intake manifold into the cylinder. The intake manifold is a system of ducts and channels that directs the air-fuel mixture to the cylinders. The proper air-fuel mixture is provided by the carburetor. In *Figure 7-1b*, the piston has just passed BDC with an air-fuel mixture in the cylinder. As the piston moves upward through the cylinder from BDC to TDC, this air-fuel mixture is compressed to a high pressure. Just before TDC, an electrical spark across the gap of the spark plug ignites the air-fuel mixture. The timing of the spark must be closely controlled.

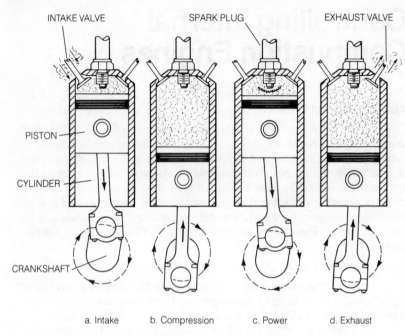

INTAKE VALVE   SPARK PLUG   EXHAUST VALVE

PISTON

CYLINDER

CRANKSHAFT

a. Intake   b. Compression   c. Power   d. Exhaust

Figure 7-1. *The 4 Strokes of a 4 Stroke/Cycle Internal Combustion
Spark-Ignited Engine*
(Source: W. B. Ribbens and N. P. Mansour, Understanding Automotive Electronics,
Texas Instruments Inc., Dec., 1981)

As the fuel burns, the hot expanding gas in the cylinder causes an
extreme rise in pressure and forces the piston downward *(Figure 7-1c)*. This is
called the power stroke because power is delivered to the crankshaft by the
piston on this stroke. When the piston reaches BDC at the end of the power
stroke *(Figure 7-1d)*, the exhaust valve opens. The piston rises in the cylinder
and forces the hot gases and combustion products out of the cylinder into the
exhaust manifold and ultimately out of the exhaust pipe into the earth's
atmosphere.

This sequence is repeated continually with power delivered to the
crankshaft on only one of the four strokes. The rotation of the shaft continues
because of the kinetic energy of the flywheel which is a large, heavy circular
mass of metal connected to the crankshaft. Note that the crankshaft rotates
through two revolutions for each four-stroke cycle and a spark occurs only
once for the two revolutions. To even out the delivery of power to the
crankshaft, more cylinders are added to the crankshaft with the power
strokes spaced in time so that power is delivered almost continuously to the
crankshaft. Besides the increase in overall power output, this is the purpose
of multi-cylinder engines such as the 4, 6 and 8-cylinder engines.

Diesel Engine

As mentioned in Chapter 2, the diesel engine operates in much the same way as the gasoline engine. The primary differences are: The much higher pressure in the cylinder, which ignites the air-fuel mixture without a spark and injection of the fuel directly in the cylinder, rather than carburetion. The same principles of controlling the internal combustion engine apply; therefore, we will not deal with the diesel engine further.

WHAT MUST BE CONTROLLED?
Control Variables

There are not many variables that can be controlled in an internal combustion engine during operation of the engine. Most of the features of the engine that affect performance are fixed during design and manufacture. For example, the volume of the cylinder, the length of the piston stroke and the maximum pressure due to compression are fixed. The size and shape of the intake manifold, the size of the valves, and the shape of the piston top also are fixed. In fact, the only operational variables of the gasoline engine that have proven practical to adjust during operation of the engine are the ignition timing and the air/fuel ratio. The standard manual control for the operation of the engine is the throttle which is controlled by the driver's depression of the accelerator pedal in an automobile.

Ignition Timing

The alternatives available for timing the ignition are shown in *Figure 7-2*. Ignition timing is measured in angular degrees of crankshaft rotation. The ignition timing can be adjusted so that spark occurs before top dead center (BTDC) as shown in *Figure 7-2a*. This is called advanced spark timing. If the spark occurs exactly at the time the piston reaches TDC, the timing is set at TDC or zero degrees. This situation is illustrated in *Figure 7-2b*. Finally, the spark could be delayed until the piston has started moving down the cylinder after it has passed TDC as shown in *Figure 7-2c*. This is called retarded timing and is measured in degrees after top dead center (ATDC).

The performance of the engine in terms of efficiency, mechanical force measured as torque at the crankshaft, and the engine exhaust emissions all depend heavily on the setting of the ignition timing. Timing that is advanced (BTDC) generally provides relatively complete combustion and high power output; however, if the timing is advanced too much, the combustion force may tend to drive the piston back down with a resulting loss of power and high mechanical stress that causes an audible pinging sound. Timing that is retarded (ATDC) can result in incomplete combustion, low power output, and overheating of the engine. Generally, engines are tuned to provide static ignition timing of about 8 to 10 degrees BTDC.

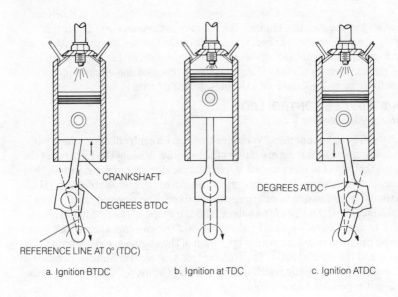

a. Ignition BTDC b. Ignition at TDC c. Ignition ATDC

Figure 7-2. Ignition Timing Possibilities

Effects of Ignition Timing

The effects of ignition timing on engine performance are shown in
Figure 7-3. Note that maximum torque occurs with advanced timing so that
ignition occurs just before TDC. Before energy conservation became so
important, torque was the most important feature of an engine's performance;
therefore, ignition timing usually was set to maximize the mechanical torque
output consistent with a smoothly running engine.

Since fuel has become expensive, the effect of spark timing on fuel
economy also has become an important factor. The effect of spark angle on fuel
economy is shown in *Figure 7-3*. Advanced timing increases the fuel efficiency
of the engine since the fuel in the cylinder has time to completely burn and
convert most of the chemical energy in the fuel into thermal and mechanical
energy in the cylinder. However, note that maximum torque and maximum
fuel efficiency do not necessarily occur with the same amount of spark
advance.

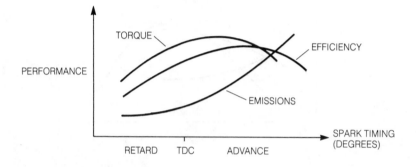

Figure 7-3. *Effect of Spark Timing on Engine Performance*

Another aspect of engine performance that has become more important is the amount of harmful combustion products in the exhaust. The main concern is the unburned hydrocarbons (HC) and the nitrous oxides (NO_x) that may be released into the atmosphere. *Figure 7-3* shows that these emissions increase as the timing is advanced. This is unfortunate since maximum power and efficiency also occur as the timing is advanced. Thus, in order to reduce these dangerous exhaust emissions, the engine control design engineer has two choices: run the engine at inefficient ignition timing or reduce emissions through some other control variable. Ideally, the other control variable should be used to reduce the hydrocarbon and nitrous oxide emissions to acceptable levels while allowing ignition timing to be adjusted for more efficient engine performance.

Air/Fuel Ratio

As mentioned earlier, the other engine control variable is the air/fuel (A/F) ratio. The A/F ratio also influences efficiency, power output, and engine exhaust emissions. The effects of the A/F ratio are shown in *Figure 7-4*. Notice that torque is near maximum at an A/F ratio of 14.7:1. This ratio is the proper ratio for stoichiometry when gasoline is the fuel. It is the ratio at which all carbon and hydrogen in the chemical fuel would be oxidized if the burning in the cylinder were perfect. An A/F ratio greater than stoichiometry is called a lean mixture since a greater amount of air (or less fuel) is in the air-fuel mixture. An A/F ratio less than stoichiometry is called a rich mixture since relatively more fuel is in the air-fuel mixture.

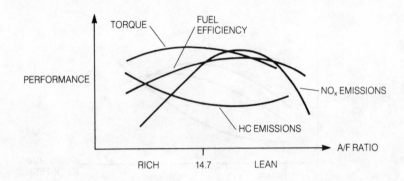

Figure 7-4. *Effect of A/F Ratio on Engine Performance*

Effects of A/F Ratio

The effect of the A/F ratio on fuel efficiency is shown in *Figure 7-4*. The miles per gallon or mileage is maximum at a relatively lean mixture, which is reasonable since less fuel is being used for only a slightly lower output torque.

The hydrocarbon emission versus the A/F ratio is shown in *Figure 7-4*. This emission increases for rich mixtures since all of the fuel will not be oxidized to water and carbon dioxide. The hydrocarbon emission is minimum at a slightly lean A/F ratio and, fortunately, this is consistent with the requirement for high fuel efficiency.

Unfortunately, the nitrous oxide emissions rise to a maximum near this point as shown in *Figure 7-4*. Either a trade-off between nitrous oxide emissions and performance must be made, or the A/F ratio must be fixed for maximum torque and efficiency with some other means used to decrease the nitrous oxide content of the exhaust.

From the information contained in *Figures 7-3* and *7-4*, it is evident that variations in ignition timing and the A/F ratio greatly affect engine performance and exhaust emissions; therefore, these variables must be controlled. The methods used to control these variables in the past before electronic controls were introduced will be discussed in the next section.

HOW HAVE INTERNAL COMBUSTION ENGINES BEEN CONTROLLED?

Most of the controls of engine operation have been mechanical, pneumatic, or hydraulic devices. Pneumatic and mechanical controls have been used to control both ignition timing and the A/F ratio. More recently a chemical system has been used to help control exhaust emissions.

Basic Ignition System

The basic electrical ignition system commonly used is shown in *Figure 7-5*. The car battery provides a low voltage source of direct current. Most cars use batteries with an output voltage of about 12 volts. When the driver operated ignition switch is in the ON position, the battery is connected to the spark generation and distribution circuit. The components that generate the high voltage that causes a spark to jump across the gap in a spark plug are the coil, the capacitor (condenser), and the breaker points.

The coil is actually a transformer that consists of a primary winding with a few turns of wire and a secondary winding with many thousands of turns of wire. This transformer increases a changing primary voltage to a higher secondary voltage. The ratio between the primary voltage and the secondary voltage is the same as the ratio between the number of turns in the primary winding and the number of turns in the secondary winding.

The breaker points provide the changing primary voltage by interrupting the flow of current through the primary winding when the points are opened. This interruption of current in the primary produces a large momentary voltage change in the primary which is multiplied by thousands of times to produce a secondary voltage of from 15,000 to 20,000 volts. This voltage is high enough to jump the gap of the spark plug to create a spark to ignite the air-fuel mixture. The capacitor is placed across the breaker points to keep a spark from forming between the points. Such a spark would reduce the secondary voltage and damage the breaker points.

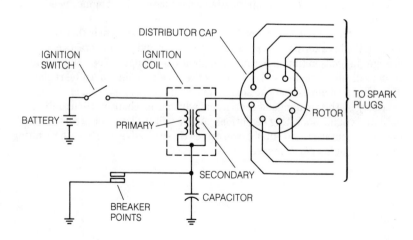

Figure 7-5. *Non-Electronic Ignition Circuit*
(*Source: W. B. Ribbens and N. P. Mansour,* Understanding Automotive Electronics, *Texas Instruments Inc., Dec., 1981*)

The high secondary voltage must be connected to the proper spark plug at the proper time. This is the purpose of the distributor shown in *Figure 7-5*. The distributor has a rotary switch (the rotor) that connects the secondary to the appropriate spark plug just before the piston reaches TDC on the compression stroke in that cylinder. The breaker points also must be opened just at the right time to produce the high secondary voltage while the secondary is connected to the spark plug. Thus, the distributor shaft operates both the breaker points and the distributor high voltage switch. Since the spark timing must be related to the piston position in the cylinder, the distributor shaft rotation must be coupled to the crankshaft. This coupling is made by mechanically connecting the distributor shaft to the camshaft which operates the intake and exhaust valves. The camshaft is driven by the crankshaft, but the camshaft rotates at one-half the speed of the crankshaft. This is because only one spark and one valve sequence is required for each cylinder for each two revolutions of the crankshaft. The initial ignition timing is set by rotating the physical position of the distributor rotor in relationship to the camshaft, and consequently, the crankshaft. The gap between open breaker points, which must be adjusted for the correct dwell time, also affects ignition timing; therefore, this gap must be adjusted before setting the timing.

Control of the ignition timing during engine operation is accomplished by two devices. The vacuum advance unit changes the ignition timing in response to engine load changes by sensing the amount of intake manifold vacuum. This unit increases the amount of spark advance as manifold pressure increases. The other device, the centrifugal advance, varies the ignition timing as engine speed varies. The spark advance is increased as engine speed increases.

One of the problems with this basic ignition system is that the normal wear of the breaker points operating mechanism and point contacts causes changes in ignition timing because the point gap changes. The point gap must be periodically adjusted and eventually the breaker points must be replaced. The other problem is that the spark timing cannot be monitored or changed precisely by the vacuum and centrifugal advance mechanisms to maintain optimum engine operating conditions. As we will see later, electronic control of spark generation and timing overcomes these disadvantages with resulting improved engine performance.

Basic Air-Fuel System

The air-fuel mixture must be controlled in both the proportion (the amount of each) of air and fuel (the A/F ratio) and the amount of the mixture delivered to the cylinders. The carburetor is the device that does both. The A/F ratio is controlled by metering rods and orifices (jets or flow openings) that control the amount of fuel that may be drawn from the fuel reservoir or bowl by the air flow through the carburetor. The size of these metering rods and orifices are chosen in design to provide the correct A/F ratio for a particular engine. The metering rod position may be controlled by intake manifold vacuum so that the A/F ratio is decreased for heavy engine loads. An accelerator pump provides an extra amount of fuel momentarily for quick acceleration. These controls are all pneumatic or mechanical.

The basic operation of the conventional automobile carburetor is shown in *Figure 7-6*. The source of air is through an air filter which removes dirt from the air. Air is drawn through the air filter and carburetor into the intake manifold by the vacuum produced in a cylinder during the intake stroke. The amount of air and fuel that is admitted to the intake manifold and thus to the cylinder is controlled by the throttle valve. The throttle valve is controlled by the accelerator pedal. When the throttle valve is in the wide open position as shown in *Figure 7-6*, the maximum amount of air and fuel is allowed to flow into the cylinder which lets the engine run at maximum speed. When the throttle valve is in the closed position, very little air and fuel is passed into the intake manifold so that the engine speed is very slow. This is called the idle position. Atmospheric pressure is present above the fuel level in the fuel reservoir which is connected by a tube to the narrowed section of the carburetor bore. The narrowed part of the carburetor bore is called a venturi. When air flows through the venturi, a low pressure area is created just above the venturi where the tube end is located. The atmospheric pressure on the fuel inside the reservoir pushes the fuel out through the tube into the air stream rushing through the carburetor bore. The rapid air stream atomizes the liquid fuel (breaks it up into droplets) and mixes it with the air. The air-fuel mixture with the correct A/F ratio then goes past the throttle valve, through the intake manifold passageway and enters the cylinder through the open intake valve.

It is possible to replace the carburetor with an electronically controlled fuel system so that more precise control is maintained over the A/F ratio on a continuous basis. Using such a system, the A/F ratio can be adjusted continually to optimize the efficiency and torque output of the engine under all operating conditions. These techniques, along with some of the means used to control exhaust emissions will be considered next.

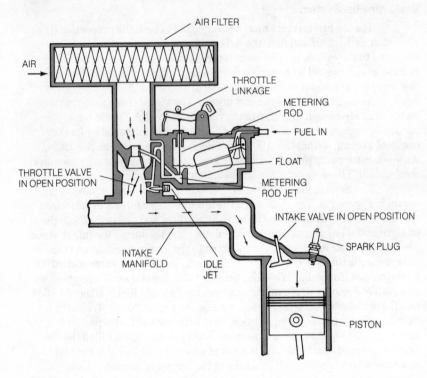

Figure 7-6. *Conventional (Non-Electronic) Carburetor and Intake Passage*

HOW CAN ELECTRONICS CONTROL AIR/FUEL RATIO?

In order to take advantage of the reliability and precision of electronic control techniques, components must be used for the A/F ratio control and the ignition timing control that can be electronically controlled. Let's consider some of these, beginning with devices to control A/F ratio.

Electronic Carburetor

In order to control the A/F ratio, an electronic carburetor *(Figure 7-7)* may be used. This carburetor is basically a modified version of the conventional carburetor. The modification consists of controlling the position of the metering rods with an electrical signal from the electronic controller. In one type of electronic carburetor, the electrical signal variations cause variations in the amount of vacuum applied to a piston connected to the metering rod. Thus, the piston positions the metering rod according to the input electrical signal variations. The position of the metering rod determines the amount of fuel that can be drawn from the carburetor by the air flow through the venturi, thereby, controlling the A/F ratio.

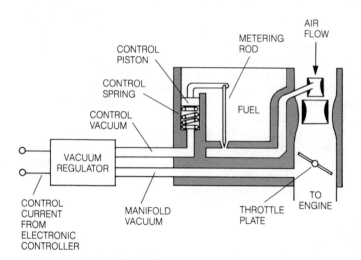

Figure 7-7. *Simplified Electronic Carburetor*
(Source: W. B. Ribbens and N. P. Mansour, Understanding Automotive Electronics,
Texas Instruments Inc., Dec., 1981)

Fuel Injection

The A/F ratio also can be controlled by using fuel injection to supply the fuel. There are three types of fuel injection: directly into the cylinder, into the intake manifold just ahead of the intake valve, or into the main inlet to the intake manifold containing the throttle valve. In order to use direct cylinder fuel injection, an expensive fuel pump is required that will develop the high pressure needed to force the fuel into the highly compressed air with precise timing. Direct cylinder injection also requires a network of fuel passages to each cylinder which add to the expense. While such injection systems are used in high performance engines, they are not cost effective for the small automobiles that are currently being developed.

The intake manifold fuel injection also is expensive since it too requires a fuel distribution system to each cylinder, although the need for extremely high fuel pressure and precise timing does not exist. A reasonable compromise between cost and good control of fuel delivery can be had by using a device to inject fuel into the intake manifold inlet where the carburetor usually is mounted. This device is called a throttle body fuel injector.

Throttle Body Fuel Injector

One type of throttle body fuel injector (TBFI) is shown in *Figure 7-8*. Fuel is delivered by the fuel pump at a relatively low pressure and the fuel pressure in the injector housing is held constant by a pressure regulator. Thus the fuel pump and pressure regulator provide a constant volume and constant pressure fuel reservoir for the injector mechanism. The injector has a spring loaded plunger that is raised by applying a control current to the injector solenoid. When the plunger is up, the pressurized fuel is forced out through the injector nozzle. Due to the pressure, it is atomized as it leaves the nozzle. When the current is removed, the spring forces the plunger down against the injector nozzle and shuts off the fuel flow. The squirt of atomized fuel mixes with the air coming from the air intake filter and passes through the intake manifold into the cylinders of the engine. The A/F ratio of the mixture can be varied from lean to rich by controlling the rate and duty cycle at which the fuel injector plunger is raised and lowered.

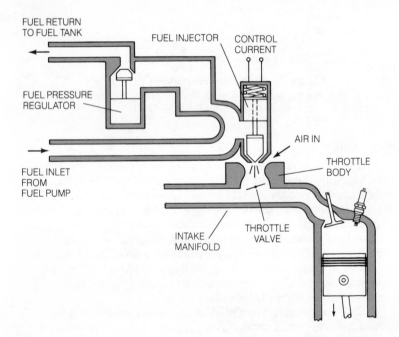

Figure 7-8. *Throttle Body Fuel Injection*
(Source: W. B. Ribbens and N. P. Mansour, Understanding Automotive Electronics, *Texas Instruments Inc., Dec., 1981)*

Duty Cycle Control

If the solenoid is pulsed with current pulses at a low rate or low duty cycle, a small amount of fuel will be injected into the air stream. Conversely, current pulses at a high rate or high duty cycle inject a larger amount of fuel. In other words, if the injector plunger is held in the open position for a longer period of time than it is held in the closed position, fuel can flow through the injector for a longer period of time. This allows a greater amount of fuel into the air stream to produce a rich A/F ratio.

The control current duty cycle to the solenoid is controlled in the manner shown in *Figure 7-9*. *Figure 7-9a* shows a control current signal that allows the fuel to flow only for a small percentage of the time. This produces a lean air-fuel mixture (high A/F ratio). *Figure 7-9b* shows the control current signal that allows fuel to flow for a large percentage of the time. This results in a rich air-fuel mixture (low A/F ratio). The percentage of the time the current

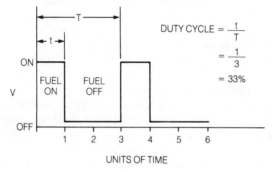

a. Duty Cycle for High A/F

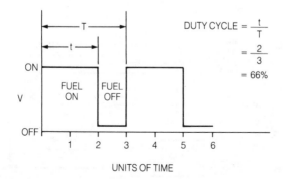

b. Duty Cycle for Low A/F

Figure 7-9. *Pulse Mode Fuel Control Signal to Fuel Metering Actuator*
(Source: W. B. Ribbens and N. P. Mansour, Understanding Automotive Electronics, Texas Instruments Inc., Dec., 1981)

is on during a given period of time is called the duty cycle of the current waveform. *Figure 7-9a* shows a 33% duty cycle waveform and *Figure 7-9b* shows a 66% duty cycle waveform. Thus, an electronic control system can control the A/F ratio by controlling the duty cycle of the control current to the TBFI solenoid.

The TBFI is not the only method for controlling the A/F ratio electronically, but it is presently the most cost effective method. Whatever method is used, the control system must determine what is the optimum A/F ratio value at all times by monitoring the performance of the engine with respect to power, efficiency, and exhaust emissions. Before we consider the full electronic control system for doing this, let's look at the electronic control of the ignition.

HOW CAN ELECTRONICS CONTROL IGNITION?

An early electronic ignition system is shown in *Figure 7-10*. Essentially, the mechanical breaker points were replaced with an electronic circuit that turns off to interrupt the current in the primary of the ignition coil to generate the secondary high voltage for the spark in the same way as the breaker points of the mechanical system. However, in the electronic system, a new scheme must be used to tell the electronic circuit when to turn off since the cam that operated the breaker points is no longer used. The unit that provides this is called a sensor as shown in *Figure 7-10*.

The sensor is a unit that determines, from the position of the distributor shaft, when to initiate the signal that triggers the electronic ignition. This sensor can be either an optical position sensor as shown in *Figure 7-11a* or a magnetic position sensor as shown in *Figure 7-11c*. In either case, the timing wheel is driven by the distributor shaft which is driven by the camshaft to establish the basic timing relation between ignition and piston position.

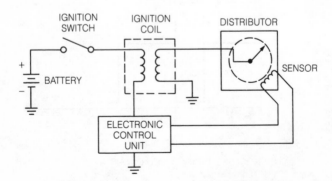

Figure 7-10. *Electronic Ignition System*
(Source: W. B. Ribbens and N. P. Mansour, Understanding Automotive Electronics, Texas Instruments Inc., Dec., 1981)

Optical Sensor

In the optical system, a light beam is cut off except when the timing wheel is in a position to let the light through an index hole. At this point, the photodetector receives light and a voltage or current pulse is generated as shown in the waveform in *Figure 7-11b*. This pulse tells the electronic control circuit when to generate a spark voltage.

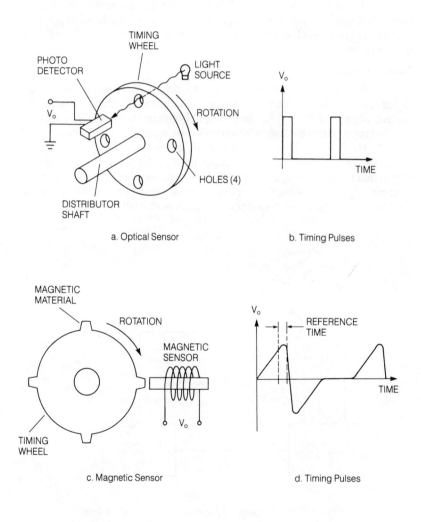

Figure 7-11. *Electronic Ignition Timing Sensors*

Magnetic Sensor

The magnetic sensor of *Figure 7-11c* produces the timing pulses shown in *Figure 7-11d* when the magnetic material in the tabs on the wheel pass by the magnetic sensor. When the sensor voltage is at its maximum is the time it triggers the electronic control circuit to generate a spark. The ignition timing is adjusted by a method similar to the mechanical breaker point system.

The principal advantage of the electronic ignition system over the mechanical ignition system is the replacement of mechanical breaker points with an electronic solid-state switching device that does not wear out with extended use.

Fully Integrated Control

In more recent automotive systems, the spark initiation and timing are integrated into the overall electronic engine control system. In such a system, shown in *Figure 7-12*, the timing pulses from the sensor are sent to the electronic engine controller which uses the timing pulses as a reference pulse for the position of the distributor shaft. From this reference signal, the electronic controller establishes an output pulse to the electronic ignition circuit that initiates the spark. Now the spark can be advanced or retarded electronically by adjusting the electronic engine controller. If one were to use electronic age jargon to describe this, the statement would be: "The electronic

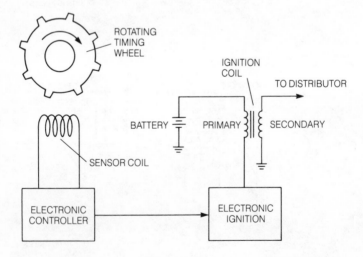

Figure 7-12. *Integrated Electronic Ignition System*
(Source: W. B. Ribbens and N. P. Mansour, Understanding Automotive Electronics, *Texas Instruments Inc., Dec., 1981)*

controller is programmed to give the correct spark timing." The circuits to accomplish this control will be discussed shortly. The major advantage of such a system, besides being solid-state, is that the timing can be adjusted much more accurately.

Future Systems

In the present production systems, the spark plug to receive the high voltage is still selected by a distributor with a rotating switch which is mechanically connected to the distributor shaft. Some experimental all-electronic systems switch the high voltage with solid-state electronic components so the mechanical distributor is not required. These may be used in production automotive systems in the near future.

HOW ARE EXHAUST EMISSIONS CONTROLLED?

Figure 7-13 is a diagram that identifies the overall engine functions within an internal combustion engine system. Air and fuel in a controlled ratio are supplied to the engine, spark timing is controlled, and the outputs are the drive shaft power and the emissions out the exhaust. Between the exhaust manifold and the emissions out the tail pipe is a catalytic converter to control emissions. In addition, part of the exhaust is returned to the intake manifold through an exhaust gas recirculation valve to help control tail pipe emissions.

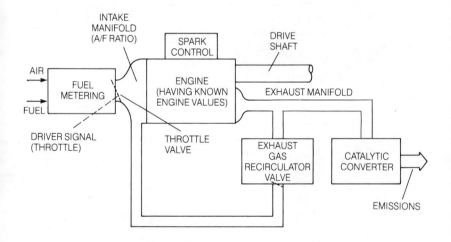

Figure 7-13. *Overall Engine Functions*
(Source: W. B. Ribbens and N. P. Mansour, Understanding Automotive Electronics, *Texas Instruments Inc., Dec., 1981)*

EGR Valve

The exhaust gas recirculation valve is used to allow a controlled amount of exhaust gas to enter the intake manifold along with the air-fuel mixture. The purpose is to lower combustion temperature which reduces nitrous oxide emissions in the exhaust. The EGR valve must be closed when the engine is idling or under heavy load. At other times, the amount of exhaust gas recirculated to the intake must be controlled based on various engine parameters. In automobiles where EGR is not electronically controlled, the EGR valve is controlled directly by intake manifold pressure and coolant temperature. Electronic control can be accomplished using the same method described in *Figures 7-8* and *7-9* for controlling the fuel injector in the TBFI. By varying the duty cycle of the current pulse to the EGR control valve solenoid shown in *Figure 7-14*, the time that the valve is open is adjusted so that the average open time allows the desired amount of exhaust to pass to the intake manifold.

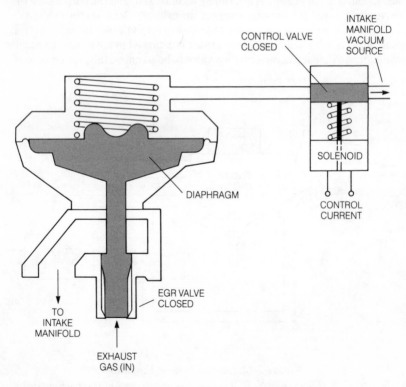

Figure 7-14. *EGR Actuator Control*
(Source: W. B. Ribbens and N. P. Mansour, Understanding Automotive Electronics, *Texas Instruments Inc., Dec., 1981)*

Catalytic Converter

The catalytic converter located in the exhaust stream between the engine and tailpipe uses chemical reactions to help control exhaust emissions. It is not subject to external controls of any kind; however, its successful operation depends upon precise control of the A/F ratio which can be achieved by electronic controls. Lets look at an electronic engine controller that includes the precise control of the A/F ratio as one of its functions.

HOW CAN ELECTRONICS CONTROL THE ENGINE?

Most electronic controllers in the future will be of the digital computer type. The concept of such a digital computer control system has been discussed previously in this book. *Figure 7-15* presents a typical microcomputer system that might be used to control an internal combustion engine.

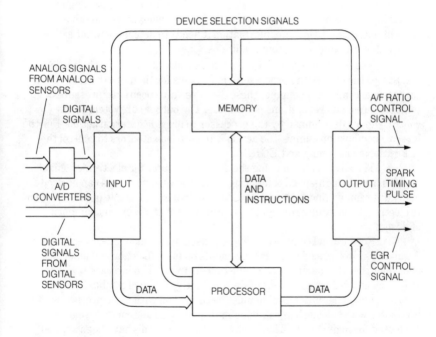

Figure 7-15. *Digital Computer System for Automotive Engine Control*

Typical Microcomputer System

As with any microcomputer system, it is made up of four main parts. The processor, typically called the CPU (central processing unit), the memory, input, and output. (The input and output functions are often referred to together as I/O.) The processor performs all the arithmetic, logic, and other program executions required by the system. It decodes, interprets and executes instructions received from a program. The processor also controls the operation of all of the other parts or subsystems of the computer system.

The memory serves two purposes. It stores the computer program that governs the behavior of the system, and it stores the data that the program and system uses. The program consists of instructions that the processor executes in the proper sequence, step by step, to perform its task. In this case, the task is that of controlling an engine. These instructions tell the computer system what to do at each point in time and under various operating conditions. The data that the memory stores or remembers is of two types, fixed or variable. The variable data consists of the current measurements of operating conditions. The fixed data includes the values stored in tables that the computer uses to look up information it needs to determine what action to take under any set of operating conditions.

The input subsystem receives measurement data from the sensors and passes the data to the processor when it asks for them. In the case of the internal combustion engine, these data are valve positions, pressures, temperatures, and revolutions per minute. The output subsystem sends control signals determined by the processor to provide external action. For the internal combustion engine, the action is to position actuators to control the A/F ratio, spark timing and EGR.

The advantages of using the digital computer for electronic control of engines include high-speed computing, versatility (same design can be used for many different engine systems), low-cost components, reliable operation even in electrically noisy environments, greater control accuracy, and simplicity of design.

For internal combustion engines used in automobiles, government regulations have placed strict requirements on fuel efficiency and exhaust emissions that the manufacturers must meet. In order to increase fuel efficiency and reduce emissions of the automotive internal combustion engine, the A/F ratio and ignition timing must be controlled with more precision than is possible with the mechanical, pneumatic and hydraulic controls that have been used for many years. That's why electronic controls have been applied. The speed and accuracy with which a microcomputer can analyze the several variable inputs, make the necessary computations and comparisons to decide what needs to be done, and produce an output control signal make it the logical choice for such a control system.

A/D and D/A Converters

Most of the input signals that represent engine RPM, intake manifold pressure, throttle angle, engine coolant temperature, intake air temperature, and EGR valve position are continuously varying (analog) signals. For the computer to detect and use these signals, they must be converted to digital codes that the processor understands. This analog-to-digital conversion is performed by a circuit called an A/D converter. Such a circuit is shown in one of the input paths in *Figure 7-15*. An alternative to using such converters is to use sensors whose output is already in the form of digital signals. These sensors with digital output may not be available for all types of measurements, but if they are, their use can significantly cut system costs.

Whichever type of input is used, the computer senses the input digital codes of the measurements and uses them in its operations. The results of these operations are used to determine the output signals which are also in digital code. In many cases, these outputs may be used directly in digital form, but it may be necessary to convert these digital codes to analog signals by using a digital-to-analog (D/A) converter circuit. This circuit performs the opposite function of the A/D converter. Again, avoiding such converters can lower system costs.

HOW DOES THE ELECTRONIC CONTROL SYSTEM WORK?

Previous discussion has shown how the fuel is regulated electronically with a TBFI to adjust A/F ratio, and has indicated that the spark is advanced or retarded electronically in order to arrive at the correct ignition timing. In addition, the EGR also is controlled to help keep harmful emissions to a minimum. All of this is done continually by the engine controller. It samples the inputs periodically, makes computations, comparisons, finds values in look-up tables, and outputs the correct digital codes or timed pulse trains to provide the correct control actuation.

It may operate in either an open-loop mode or closed-loop mode. The basic difference between them is that the closed-loop mode has error correction feedback from the output to input whereas the open-loop system does not have feedback.

Air/Fuel Ratio Control During the Open-Loop Mode

In an automobile engine, recall that the total amount of air drawn into the engine is determined by the position of the throttle valve which is in the main air passage into the intake manifold of the engine. It is controlled by the driver pressing on the accelerator pedal and is the driver's only input to the control system. Since the air volume is controlled by means external to the electronic control system, the system computes the volume of air entering the engine on the basis of parameters that it can measure as inputs and adjusts the control current for the fuel injection to give the correct A/F ratio.

The basic control system configuration is shown in *Figure 7-16*. This configuration is an open-loop control system since it uses only system input variables to generate a desired output variable without feedback. This particular control system monitors the input air temperature, the engine coolant temperature, the intake manifold pressure, the exhaust gas recirculation, the engine speed and the throttle angle. Each of these sensors produces a voltage or current output that is related to the quantity being measured in a way known by the processor and controlled by the program stored in the system memory. Whenever necessary, the sensor currents or voltages are amplified or converted to digital signal equivalents by an A/D converter. As shown in *Figure 7-16*, the computer then uses the appropriate values to determine the duty cycle of the pulsed control signal to the TBFI to provide the required A/F ratio.

For relatively constant vehicle speed, the system holds the A/F ratio close to the desired value of 14.7 (stoichiometry) which provides reasonable fuel efficiency and power output with a low level of hydrocarbon emissions.

The open-loop mode is generally used for engine starting and engine warm-up conditions during which power output, efficiency, and emissions do not have to be controlled precisely. After the engine is fully warmed up, the control system switches to the closed-loop mode where maximum efficiency and minimum exhaust emissions are obtained.

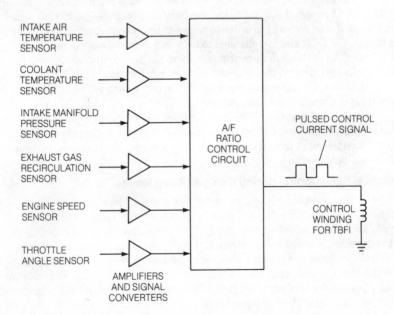

Figure 7-16. Open-Loop A/F Ratio Control

Open-loop A/F ratio control also is used at other times when an A/F ratio of 14.7 is not suitable. During periods of fast acceleration, the A/F ratio must be adjusted to a rich mixture to obtain more power. The control system senses the acceleration condition by monitoring throttle position, rate of change of throttle position, and intake manifold pressure. When the proper combination of these variables exist, the A/F ratio is dropped to a value that produces maximum torque for the engine while fuel efficiency and exhaust emissions are momentarily ignored.

The opposite case occurs during deceleration and idling. In this case, a lean mixture must be maintained. The control system senses deceleration by monitoring the same variables as for acceleration. When this condition is sensed, the fuel delivery rate is slowed and may even be shut off completely for a few seconds. The idle condition is sensed by throttle position and RPM. The control system maintains the idle speed at a constant RPM that has been determined to provide the best compromise between fuel consumption and exhaust emissions. The control system continually adjusts the idle speed as loads such as the air conditioner are switched on and off.

Air/Fuel Ratio Control During the Closed-Loop Mode

Once the engine is warmed up and operating with only small variations in vehicle speed and mild acceleration, the control system switches to the closed-loop mode. In this mode, the control system can closely control the A/F ratio so that the average A/F ratio is at 14.7. This operating point is chosen because it provides good fuel efficiency and produces the best compromise for exhaust emissions. With this level of exhaust emissions from the engine, a catalytic converter can reduce the exhaust emissions out the tailpipe to less than the regulation levels.

In order to use a control system in a closed-loop configuration, some aspect of system output, in this case the A/F ratio, must be monitored and the results fed back to the input. The feedback signal is compared to the desired output and an error signal is applied to the control electronics so proper adjustment can be made at the input. A closed-loop system that can achieve this in an internal combustion engine is shown in *Figure 7-17*.

This system maintains the average A/F ratio at 14.7 to provide good fuel efficiency and produce exhaust emissions that are optimum for the catalytic converter to handle. *Figure 7-18* shows the narrow range of the A/F ratio around 14.7 (stoichiometry) where the catalytic converter is fairly efficient in converting all three harmful exhaust emissions; nitrous oxides (NO_x), carbon monoxide (CO) and hydrocarbons (HC), to acceptable levels. Notice in *Figure 7-17* that the system still needs all of the input variables to set the basic A/F ratio as discussed for the open-loop system. The feedback and error correction signal only "fine tune" the A/F ratio.

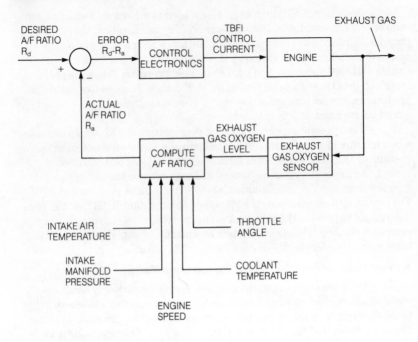

Figure 7-17. *Closed-Loop A/F Ratio Controller Structure*

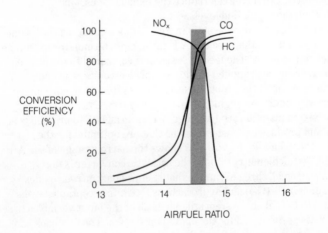

Figure 7-18. *Typical Conversion Efficiency of a Three-Way Catalytic Converter*
(Source: W. B. Ribbens and N. P. Mansour, Understanding Automotive Electronics, *Texas Instruments Inc., Dec., 1981)*

Exhaust Gas Oxygen Sensor

The predominant method presently used to indirectly measure the actual A/F ratio is to place an oxygen sensor in the exhaust manifold. One commonly used exhaust gas oxygen (EGO) sensor is made from zirconia oxide. The typical characteristics of this sensor are shown in *Figure 7-19*. The important characteristic of this type of sensor is that it indicates the oxygen content of the exhaust gas which is related to the A/F ratio. When the oxygen sensor has a low voltage output, it indicates that the oxygen content of the exhaust is high which indicates a lean mixture (high A/F ratio). Conversely, when the output of the sensor is a high voltage, there is little or no oxygen in the exhaust, indicating a rich mixture (low A/F ratio). The sensor is designed to switch rapidly and sharply with only small variations in oxygen content around stoichiometry.

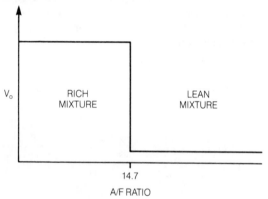

a. Ideal EGO Sensor Characteristics

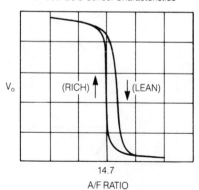

b. Typical EGO Sensor Characteristics

Figure 7-19. *Zirconia Oxide EGO Sensor Characteristics*
(*Source: W. B. Ribbens and N. P. Mansour,* Understanding Automotive Electronics, *Texas Instruments Inc., Dec., 1981*)

The control system monitors the signal from the oxygen sensor. If it has switched to a low voltage indicating a lean mixture, the control system increases the duty cycle of the pulsed signal to the TBFI so that the A/F ratio is decreased to make a rich mixture. If it is a high voltage indicating a rich mixture, the control system decreases the duty cycle of the pulsed signal to the TBFI so that the A/F ratio is increased for a lean mixture.

Since it takes a certain time for a change in A/F ratio at the intake to show up in the exhaust oxygen content, the A/F ratio will vary from slightly high to slightly low as the oxygen sensor switches back and forth *(Figure 7-20)*. Thus, the A/F ratio will constantly vary around 14.7 to maintain an *average* operating point of stoichiometry, which is the desired result.

Unfortunately, this closed-loop system can only work when the exhaust gas temperature is above 300 degrees Celsius because the EGO sensor does not perform properly below that temperature. That is why the control system must operate in the open-loop mode during the engine warm up. However, as mentioned earlier, the control system also attempts to hold the A/F ratio close to stoichiometry during open-loop operation.

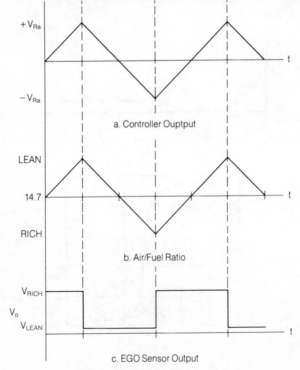

Figure 7-20. *Simplified Waveforms in a Closed-Loop Fuel Control System* (Source: W. B. Ribbens and N. P. Mansour, Understanding Automotive Electronics, *Texas Instruments Inc., Dec., 1981*)

Ignition Timing Control

The other variable that the electronic control system must control is the spark timing. At the present time, most electronic ignition controllers always operate in the open-loop mode because there is no reliable sensor to provide the required feedback for the closed-loop mode.

As previously mentioned, the basic timing is set by the mechanical coupling between crankshaft and distributor shaft. This basic timing is used for engine starting. After the engine starts, the amount of spark advance required depends on barometric pressure, intake manifold pressure, engine speed, and engine temperature. Notice that these same inputs are required for adjusting the A/F ratio; thus, the same sensors can be used for ignition control. In some systems, a separate sensor is provided for barometric pressure; however, intake manifold pressure before the engine is started can be used for this value.

While the relationships for spark advance as a function of these variables are complex and vary from engine to engine, it is possible to determine them by actual measurement on test engines and store them in tables in the computer memory of the control system.

A block diagram of the spark advance portion of the control system is shown in *Figure 7-21*. The output of the controller is the signal that activates the electronic ignition switch which interrupts the primary coil current to produce the spark voltage. Notice that there is a reference timing pulse input obtained from the timing wheel sensor previously discussed in *Figure 7-11*. In order for the spark advance to be controlled electronically on a continual basis, the time to generate a spark must be determined by the control system using the information from the engine sensors and the timing pulses produced by the timing wheel.

Computing Spark Advance

The basic idea is illustrated in *Figure 7-22*. The pulses shown in *Figure 7-22a* are produced by the timing wheel sensor. The pulses shown in *Figure 7-22b* are the output pulses from the spark timing control circuit when the timing for the spark has been set for a particular advance angle. The control circuit simply has to delay the generation of the spark for the next cylinder by the time T_d shown in the figure. For spark advance, T_d will be only slightly less than T, the time interval of the timing pulses. T is the reciprocal of the RPM of the timing wheel multiplied by the number of tabs or holes (which correspond to the number of cylinders in the engine) on the timing wheel.

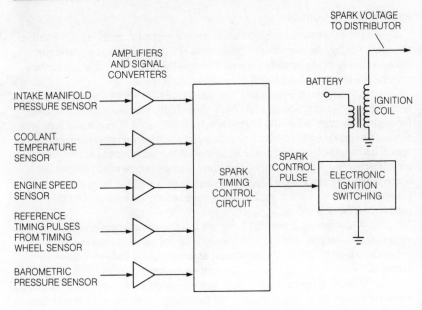

Figure 7-21. Open-Loop Spark Control

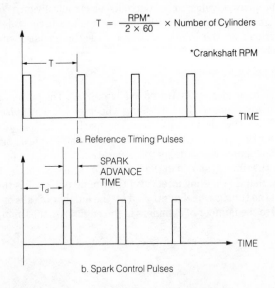

Figure 7-22. Generation of Spark Control Pulses for Spark Advance

Let's take an example. If the engine crankshaft is rotating at 3000 RPM, the timing wheel rotates at 1500 RPM (camshaft speed) or 25 revolutions per second. For a 4-cylinder engine, four pulses must be generated per revolution or 100 pulses per second. One pulse is generated every 1/100 of a second (10 milliseconds); thus, T = 10 milliseconds for this case. Therefore, the delay, T_d, between the timing pulse and the generation of the spark voltage must be something less than 10 milliseconds. A digital computer control system could handle this task by computing T from the RPM input and then computing T_d from the desired spark angle input from a table.

Look-Up Tables

Another way that T_d can be determined is by using look-up tables that give T_d directly indexed to RPM. *Figure 7-23* shows part of a table that relates RPM to T_d where T_d is represented by a counter value for a given firing angle. Different tables may be used depending on whether the engine is fully warmed up or not. The table shown in *Figure 7-23* is for the example of a 4-cylinder engine running at 3000 RPM.

The computer program searches the RPM table until it finds the speed range that includes 3000 RPM. The RPM index points to the value of 990 in the counter value table. This might represent a T_d of 9.9 milliseconds. This value of 990 is loaded into the counter (step 1). When the reference timing pulse occurs (step 2), the clock signal decrements the counter (step 3) until the value of 00 is reached. At this time (step 4), the controller sends a pulse to the electronic ignition circuit which then generates the spark voltage.

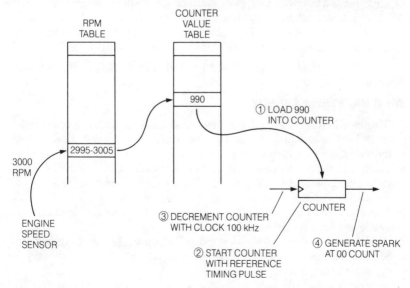

Figure 7-23. *Tables Used in Digital Controllers to Determine Spark Angle*

The same method can be used to adjust the spark advance for changes in engine load as indicated by the changes in intake manifold pressure. In this case, the computer program would search a manifold pressure index to find the appropriate counter value. The computer would add this value to the value found from the RPM index and the sum would be loaded into the counter.

Notice that this whole process is controlled by a computer program and that the spark advance information is stored in tables in the computer memory. Since this memory is simply a plug-in integrated circuit, it is just a matter of changing this memory IC to change the spark advance information. For example, if the engine to be controlled is an 8-cylinder engine with the same amount of advance as required by the 4-cylinder engine at 3000 RPM, the only change that would have to be made in the entire control system would be to change the table values by replacing one memory circuit with another. Thus, the 8-cylinder table would simply have 495 (one-half of 990 because of twice as many cylinders) corresponding to 3000 RPM instead of 990. The advantage of the digital computer control system is obvious. The system does not have to be redesigned for each new or different engine; just a few of the plug-in memory circuits have to be changed to change the operational control tables in the system.

There are other facets of electronic engine control that are beyond the scope of this book. Control systems that provide constant vehicle speed (cruise control systems) and constant engine speed (governors) also have an impact on engine performance and efficiency. Related electronic control systems that are used to provide good traction and anti-skid action during acceleration and braking on slippery surfaces do not affect energy utilization, but do affect automobile safety. Information about these related control systems as well as details on the engine control concepts presented in this chapter are contained in another book in this Understanding Series™:

Understanding Automotive Electronics, by William B. Ribbens and Norman P. Mansour.

WHAT HAVE WE LEARNED?

1. Gasoline-fueled, spark-ignited engines used in automobiles need electronic control so that automobile manufacturers can meet government regulations for fuel efficiency and exhaust emission.
2. Electronic control systems for internal combustion engines operate open-loop or closed-loop depending on whether the mode is start-up, idle, warm-up, continuous run, acceleration or deceleration.
3. Important variables that must be controlled are air/fuel ratio, ignition timing and exhaust emissions.
4. Digital electronic control allows standardized hardware control systems to be used that can be varied for different applications by changing the way the system is programmed.

Quiz for Chapter 7

1. What are the differences between a spark-ignited and diesel engine?
   a. the spark-ignited engine uses fossil fuel while a diesel engine does not.
   b. the diesel engine has much lower cylinder pressure.
   c. the diesel engine does not use a spark to ignite the fuel mixture.
   d. the diesel engine does not use valves to exhaust combustion products while the spark-ignited engine does.

2. Ignition timing of a spark-ignited engine is usually adjusted to occur:
   a. as the piston reaches the top of its stroke.
   b. just before the piston reaches the top of its stroke.
   c. just after the piston reaches the top of its stroke.

3. Stoichiometry refers to an air/fuel ratio that:
   a. maximizes engine torque output.
   b. maximizes engine fuel efficiency.
   c. provides for the most complete combustion of the fuel in the engine.
   d. reduces nitrous oxide emissions to a minimum level.

4. The purpose of the breaker points in a non-electronic ignition system is to:
   a. distribute the spark to the appropriate spark plug.
   b. generate a high voltage signal.
   c. protect distributor contacts from excessive wear.
   d. interrupt the ignition coil primary current.

5. The purpose of the condenser or capacitor in a non-electronic ignition system is to:
   a. generate a high voltage signal.
   b. protect the breaker points from electrical damage.
   c. protect distributor contacts from electrical damage.
   d. interrupt the ignition coil primary current.

6. In an electronic ignition system, the electronic switch replaces the:
   a. breaker points.
   b. condenser.
   c. distributor.
   d. ignition coil.

7. The voltage generated by the secondary of the ignition coil is in the range of (thousands of volts):
   a. 2 to 5.
   b. 5 to 10.
   c. 10 to 15.
   d. 15 and above.

8. In a conventional carburetor, the venturi is:
   a. a narrowing of the air passage to provide a pressure reduction.
   b. a device that maintains the fuel level in the carburetor.
   c. a filtering device.
   d. a tube through which fuel flows.

9. In a throttle body fuel injection carburetor, a duty cycle of 50% is found to provide too low a fuel flow to maintain the desired A/F ratio. The duty cycle should be:
   a. increased.
   b. decreased.
   c. unchanged.

10. A magnetic position sensor provides the same information as an optical sensor except it produces:
    a. a square pulse.
    b. a current pulse that flows only in one direction.
    c. twice as many pulses per cylinder.
    d. a non-rectangular and bi-directional pulse.

11. During the start-up phase of an electronically controlled engine, the control system is operated in open-loop because:
   a. the exhaust gas oxygen sensor does not work until the engine gets hot.
   b. there is no feedback signal that will indicate the A/F ratio.
   c. there are no significant emissions from a cold engine.
   d. all of the above.
   e. a and b above.

12. If a catalytic converter is used, an A/F ratio of 14 would typically result in how much (in percent) of the hydrocarbon emissions being eliminated from the exhaust?
   a. less than 10
   b. 25
   c. 70
   d. over 80

13. In the situation of problem 12, what percentage of the nitrous oxide emissions will be removed from the exhaust?
   a. less than 10
   b. 25
   c. 70
   d. over 80

14. The voltage out of a typical EGO sensor changes:
   a. gradually as the A/F ratio changes.
   b. very rapidly as the A/F ratio varies through stoichiometry.
   c. not at all with A/F ratio.

15. An 8-cylinder engine operating at 1800 rpm would produce pulses from an engine speed sensor once every how many milliseconds?
   a. 0.5
   b. 2.33
   c. 8.33
   d. 12.5

16. For the example of *Figure 7-23*, what number would correspond to a 0 degree advance in timing?
   a. 198
   b. 900
   c. 1000
   d. 1980

17. Under which of the following conditions would open-loop control of the A/F ratio be used?
   a. idle of hot engine
   b. constant speed highway driving of hot engine
   c. acceleration
   d. all of the above

18. A portion of the exhaust gas is recirculated through the cylinders to:
   a. provide more complete combustion.
   b. increase the combustion temperature.
   c. decrease the combustion temperature.
   d. reduce the levels of hydrocarbon emissions.

19. The effect of recirculating exhaust gas back through the cylinders is to:
   a. increase fuel efficiency.
   b. increase power.
   c. reduce hydrocarbon emissions.
   d. reduce nitrous oxide emissions.
   e. c and d above.

20. The purpose of the catalytic converter is to:
   a. increase fuel efficiency.
   b. increase engine power.
   c. reduce exhaust emissions.
   d. purify the fuel.

How Nuclear Energy is Controlled

ABOUT THIS CHAPTER

Nuclear energy holds great promise in providing long term solutions for our future energy needs. However, nuclear energy also tends to arouse fear in many people, possibly because they have a clear appreciation for the awesome power of the atom as demonstrated by the atomic bomb. The key to making nuclear energy acceptable to the general public is to ensure its safety. Electronic control techniques are used to make certain the nuclear giant is kept in harness so that its tremendous potential serves the people without causing environmental damage that would be harmful to life. Several of the control problems associated with nuclear energy will be examined in this chapter.

WHAT ARE THE FORMS OF NUCLEAR ENERGY?

As discussed in Chapter 2, the basic forms of nuclear energy are the energy of fission and the energy of fusion. Both are based on the fact that mass can be converted to energy, and that only a small amount of mass is required to produce tremendous amounts of energy.

Fission

In the case of atomic fission, an atom is converted to an unstable element by bombarding the nucleus with neutrons. The unstable element then splits, or fissions, resulting in the formation of more neutrons and two or more other elements of lower atomic weight (smaller number of neutrons and protrons in the nucleus) than the original unstable element. The mass of the products of the reaction is less than the initial mass of the initial atom and its triggering neutron. The loss in mass shows up in a large release of energy.

As pointed out in Chapter 2, for each kilogram of mass lost, 85.3 trillion BTUs or 25 billion kilowatt-hours of energy is generated. A kilogram released as nuclear energy is equivalent to over 3 billion times the energy released in a kilogram of materials that result in chemical energy reactions.

Non-Breeder Reaction

An example of nuclear fission was discussed in Chapter 2 (*Figure 2.2*). A similar figure is presented as *Figure 8-1*, with the different energy components listed as percentages of the overall energy released. Recall that a uranium atom was bombarded with a neutron, produced two neutrons, seven electrons and two other atoms, lanthanum and molybdenum. The majority of the released energy, about 80%, is in the form of increased kinetic energy of the resulting atoms. This energy can be converted to thermal energy as the particles are slowed down in the surrounding heat transfer fluid. About 15% of the fission energy appears in the form of high energy electrons (beta particles) and the resulting gamma ray radiation. The remaining 5% of the released energy is associated with increased kinetic energy of the resulting neutrons. Certain types of nuclear reactions need such high energy neutrons for successful fission. However, the reaction shown in *Figure 8-1* requires relatively low energy (slow neutrons) for efficient reactions. Thus, a reactor using the process of *Figure 8-1* requires a material between adjacent volumes of uranium atoms to slow down the reaction neutrons. Such a material is called a moderator. Water is commonly used as both the moderator and the heat transfer fluid in the lower temperature reactors. The overall reaction is kept under control by the introduction of neutron absorbing materials (control rods or chemicals mixed in the moderator) into the fission materials.

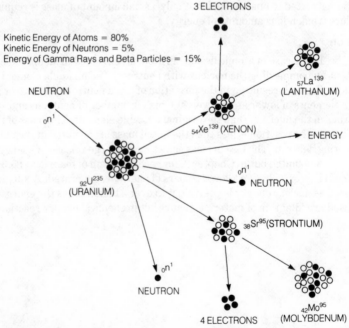

Figure 8-1. Fission of U^{235}

Breeder Reaction

Another type of fission reaction is shown in *Figure 8-2*. This is the reaction used in fast breeder reactors. These reactors are called breeder reactors because they generate more of the same fuel that they use in producing energy. This can be seen by examining the reactions shown in *Figure 8-2*. The fuel in this case is plutonium (Pu^{239}) which, when bombarded by a neutron, splits into two fission atoms and typically 3 neutrons. One of these fast neutrons can be used to cause the next fission to occur while the two other neutrons are not needed to sustain the chain reaction. If these two "extra" neutrons are sent into a material rich in uranium (U^{238}), then two more plutonium atoms can be produced. This means that for each atom used to produce energy, two new fissionable atoms are produced. Of course, this assumes ideal conditions. In practice, an average of less than two neutrons and between one and two atoms of new plutonium is produced for each plutonium atom used for thermal energy generation.

The required structure is shown in *Figure 8-2* with the fission energy generating material consisting of around 20% plutonium and 80% uranium oxide. The breeder material consists of all uranium oxide (which contains the U^{238}), which will be converted to plutonium over time. The reaction rate can be controlled by placing neutron absorbing control rods between the adjacent areas of the fission energy producing materials, just as it is in non-breeder reactors. Thus, the fission breeder reactor has the advantage over non-breeder reactors in that it can generate new nuclear fuel as it produces energy.

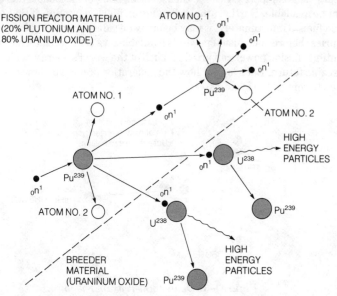

Figure 8-2. *Fission and Breeding of Pu^{239}*

As with non-breeder reactors, the kinetic energy of the fission produced atoms is converted into thermal energy by a surrounding absorbing liquid. Generally, in breeder reactors, the heat transport fluid is liquid sodium instead of water. Further, since high energy or fast neutrons are required in the reaction, the breeder reactor does not use any moderator materials.

Fusion

The final type of nuclear reaction is that of nuclear fusion. At present, commercial fusion reactors are not available, but much research is underway to provide the technology to build such reactors.

One simple fusion reaction is shown in *Figure 8-3*. This is the deuterium-tritium reaction that produces helium and a high energy neutron. The neutron can be used to provide thermal energy for the generation of steam. The energy is developed because the mass of the products of the reaction is less than the mass of the deuterium and tritium so that a large amount of kinetic energy is released in the reaction. The fusion reaction can be maintained only if sufficient gas densities and temperatures can be sustained. At the present time, it is only possible to meet these conditions under the uncontrolled conditions of a bomb. A controlled reaction for power generation is not yet feasible.

The overwhelming advantage of the fusion reaction is that the fuels are very plentiful. Deuterium is found in such abundance in the oceans of the world that such a power source would provide world energy needs for billions of years. This compares with the thousands of years of fissionable fuel that might be available. Further, the cost of fusion fuel is a fraction of that of the fission fuels. Unfortunately, it may be many decades, or possibly even centuries, before such fusion power is available on a commercial scale. In the meantime, fission power can provide much of the world's energy needs for the forseeable future. Let's look at how the generation occurs and how electronics is used to control the systems.

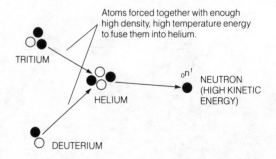

Figure 8-3. *Deuterium-Tritium Fusion*

HOW DOES A NUCLEAR POWER PLANT WORK?

A nuclear power plant uses a nuclear fission reaction to generate the thermal energy which is then converted to mechanical and electrical energy. The design of a nuclear fission electrical power plant involves the methods that are used to control the rate of nuclear reactions (the number of fissions per unit time per unit volume) and the power plant methods used to remove the thermal energy to produce steam to drive a steam turbine which generates mechanical or electrical energy. The overall plant structure is shown in *Figure 8-4*. The reactor vessel contains the fission material, coolant flow paths, and neutron absorbing control rods. In liquid water reactors, the coolant fluid also serves as a neutron absorbing moderator to further control the fission reaction. The possibly radioactive heat transport fluid removes heat from the hot core and delivers it to the heat exchanger in the boiler that produces the steam. The cooler return fluid from the heat exchanger cools the reactor to keep its temperature within safe limits.

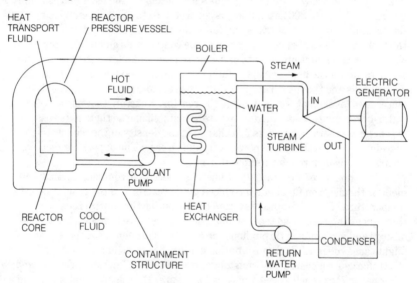

Figure 8-4. *Nuclear Electrical Power Plant*

The water in the boiler is converted to steam by the hot reactor fluid flowing through the heat exchanger. This steam drives the steam turbine which in turn drives the electrical generator. The exhaust steam from the turbine is condensed and the water is returned to the boiler. The heat transport fluid, very commonly water, is maintained in a closed protected system to avoid releasing any radioactive material into the environment. The containment structure is constructed in such a manner that it shields the radioactive material to reduce radiation exposure to acceptable levels and contains the radioactive material to prevent radioactivity from escaping to the environment. Since the nuclear reaction is one of atomic particles and since electronics is based on the use of and detection and control of atomic particles (electrons), it is only natural that electronics plays an important part in controlling and maintaining nuclear reactions so unplanned release of radioactive material does not occur.

Reactor Core

The reactor consists of a core of fissionable material in the form of fuel assemblies placed in an array structure of about 300 rods as shown in *Figure 8-5*. Each fuel rod is separated from others in the assembly by spacers so that the heat transport fluid can flow through the assembly and cool it. As stated previously, if the heat transport fluid is also a moderator, the purpose of the moderator is to slow down the high speed neutrons resulting from the fission to a level where the probability for absorption, and hence fission, is the greatest. Each array of fuel rods forms a fuel assembly and each fuel assembly (there may be up to 200 assemblies) is separated from other assemblies by flow channels for the heat transport fluid. Control rods extend down into the fuel assemblies at specific locations. The control rods and moderator characteristics maintain the rate of fission reactions at a level to maintain the temperature of the heat transport fluid to within desired levels. Without the control rods and the heat transport fluid, the reactor temperature would increase to levels that would damage the reactor. Reactors that use a water-boron mixture as a moderator are self-stabilizing so that an increase in reactor temperature results in a change in the density of the moderator; therefore, the reactivity and power output decrease. The opposite effect occurs for a drop in reactor temperature.

Thus, two important functions of an electronic control system are to monitor the neutron flux being produced in the reactor and the reactor coolant temperature. Then the control system must position the control rods throughout the reactor so that the neutron rate and core temperature are as desired and are uniform throughout the core. This prevents hot spots that might cause too much fuel consumption in a small portion of the reactor. The electronic control system also must monitor the coolant flow and pressure and other parameters such as reactor vessel pressure. If these parameters should reach unacceptable operating values, the control system must shut down the reactor by inserting all control rods fully into the core and possibly provide, if conditions warranted, emergency cooling water to the core structure. Failure to do this could result in the melting of the core. This is the worst kind of failure or accident that can occur in a fission reactor. (It is also a very unlikely failure.) Atomic explosion is not possible since the nuclear fuel is not sufficiently concentrated to produce a catastrophic chain reaction. Even in the case where the reactor must be shut down, the principle safety concern is to limit or avoid the leakage of radioactive material to the surrounding environment.

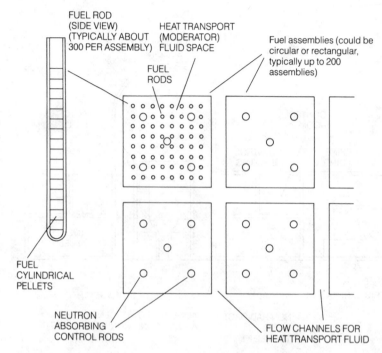

Figure 8-5. *Portion of Reactor Core (Top View)*

Plant Layout

The overall nuclear electrical power plant design depends on which type of reactor is being used. The principle types are the pressurized water reactor (PWR), the boiling water reactor (BWR), and the fast breeder reactor (FBR). The general structure of the plant usually has the basic features of *Figure 8-4*; however, *Figure 8-6* indicates some of the other facilities of a nuclear plant. In this case, the layout is that of a typical PWR or BWR.

The main containment building houses the reactor in the reactor vessel. An internal concrete structure supports the reactor vessel. Next to the containment building is the fuel building where both new fuel and spent fuel assemblies are stored. On the other side of the containment building are the control building, auxiliary building and safeguards. These buildings house the control center, offices, and auxiliary power generating equipment (diesel-powered generators and batteries) that will power control systems in emergency situations when normal power is lost. The remaining building shown in *Figure 8-6* is the turbine building which houses the steam turbines and electric generators.

Much of the information presented in *Figures 8-4* and *8-6* applies in general to all types of reactors. Of course, details of the design vary for each type of reactor. Let's discuss a few of these details.

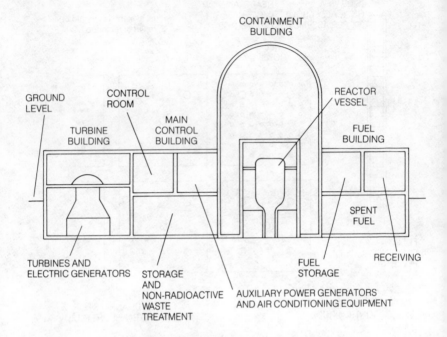

Figure 8-6. Typical Nuclear Plant Layout

Boiling Water Reactor

A BWR would probably use a core of the type shown in *Figure 8-5* and a plant of the type shown in *Figure 8-6*. However, since the water in the reactor is allowed to boil to produce steam, this steam could be used directly to drive the turbine without going through a heat exchanger as shown in *Figure 8-4*. For a BWR, the reactor vessel must withstand internal pressures of up to 1,500 pounds per square inch. Coolant water is pumped down around the reactor core and flows up through the core vertically as it is heated and converted into steam at typically less than 700°F. In order to reduce contamination and deterioration of the turbine blades, the steam is collected from the top of the reactor and dried. Any radioactivity that exists in the turbine steam is of low half-life so that it is quite easy to regulate and control the condensate so there is no danger of radioactivity exposure to the environment.

Pressurized Water Reactor

The PWR reactor vessel must withstand higher pressure than the BWR vessel—over 2,000 pounds per square inch—to keep the water in the reactor in its liquid state, even at the hot liquid outlet temperature of around 600°F. The return coolant water is at around 540°F and the volume rate of circulation is quite high—hundreds of thousands of gallons per minute. The heat exchanger, as shown in *Figure 8-4*, is needed to transfer the hot reactor water heat to the boiler water. The coolant consists of water which contains a certain percentage of boron concentration. The higher the boron concentration, the slower the neutrons in the reactor and vice-versa. By modifying the boron concentration, the power output of the reactor can be controlled. The boron concentration also determines the effective control range of the control rods. The boron concentration is changed as the reactor fuel is consumed to maintain reactor control and reaction uniformity within desired limits.

Inert Gas Reactor

Another type of reactor uses an inert gas such as helium to cool the reactor. In this case, larger coolant flow holes are used in the core to provide the passages for the large volumes of gas flow required. The hot gas going to the heat exchanger in the boiler is in the range of 1400°F, producing steam in the range of 1000°F. The return helium from the boiler is in the range of 600°F to 700°F. In this case, the pressure on the reactor vessel is much lower, typically in the range of 400 to 700 pounds per square inch.

Fast Breeder Reactor

The FBR generally uses liquid sodium as the coolant and heat transport fluid. In this case, the internal reactor and piping materials must not react chemically with the hot sodium. The hot sodium leaving the reactor is at about 1000°F, as is the hot steam generated for the turbine. The cool liquid sodium that is pumped back through the reactor core is at about 800°F. In all of these reactors, the electronic control systems must maintain the proper reaction rate, reactor temperature, and coolant flow to safely and efficiently produce the amount of electrical power needed. Let's look at some of these electronic control systems.

HOW IS NUCLEAR ENERGY CONTROLLED ELECTRONICALLY?

Electronic control and monitoring of reaction rates, core temperature, coolant flow and temperature, reactor vessel pressure, and radioactivity are required in a nuclear plant to control precisely the output of the reactor and to keep all systems in safe and efficient operating regions. Positioning the control rods and regulating the coolant properties are the main means of maintaining operating conditions within desired ranges. Full rod insertion and activation of emergency cooling equipment are also functions of the electronic control system to provide safety in case critical system failures are detected.

Reactor Control

The control of the reactor core activity is the primary control function. The basic elements of instrumentation and actuators involved are shown in *Figure 8-7*. The coolant pump and flow channel arrangement causes relatively cool fluid to flow down the sides of the reactor vessel and up through the core. The fluid is heated as it passes through the core and the hot fluid is sent to the heat exchanger in the boiler. The operation and control of the cooling system will be considered later.

The reactor operation and the temperature of the transport fluid is controlled by fine positioning of the control rods and by controlling the boron concentration in the coolant of pressurized water reactors. When the neutron absorbing rods are fully withdrawn, the maximum reaction rate can occur.

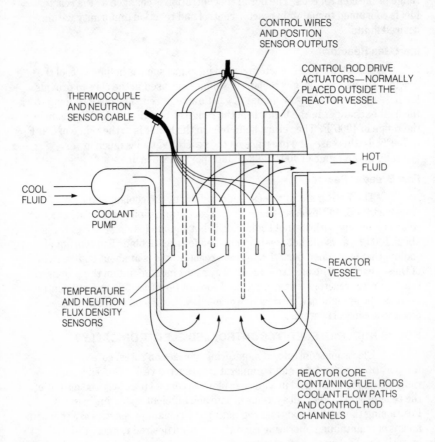

Figure 8-7. *Reactor Instrumentation*

When they are fully extended into the core, they reduce the internal reactions and temperature generation to a minimum. Generally, all of the rods are positioned at about the same vertical level within the core to deliver the needed fluid temperature to the heat exchanger. As the load (power demand) decreases, this temperature is reduced by inserting the rods further into the core. As the load (power demand) increases, or as fuel is consumed in the lower portions of the core, the rods are withdrawn from the core to increase the active reaction area which increases the thermal output of the reactor.

The control system must know at all times the current position of the rods and the temperature and neutron flux profile across the entire core; thus, there are temperature sensors (thermocouples) and neutron flux density sensors positioned throughout the core. The signals produced by these devices are sent through the sensor instrumentation cable to the control system electronics. Similarly, the position information signals for the control rods are sent to the control system electronics though the rod position sensor cable. The control system then generates signals which activate the rod drive mechanism to adjust the rod positions.

Basic Control Electronics

A block diagram of the basic electronic controls that interface with the signals of *Figure 8-7* are shown in *Figure 8-8*. The rod control is split into three groups. One group is positioned in critical locations in the core. This group is inserted all the way into the core to shut down the nuclear reactions. A second group is inserted all the way into the core to stop the excessive generation of neutrons, but not shut down the entire core. The third group of rods are gradually changed in position to provide fine control of reactor output power to adjust for power system load changes. The electronics for each group of rods monitors the outputs of the temperature and neutron flux sensors in the core.

The average temperature and average neutron flux are compared to preset limits to determine if a shutdown or high neutron flux condition exists. If they do, the full length of the appropriate group of control rods is inserted into the core at a rapid rate. If neither limit condition exists, but signals from the turbine(s) indicate the need to stop the flow of steam to the turbine(s), the steam valves will be opened to bypass the turbine(s).

If none of these conditions exist, the rod control electronics compares the current average temperature with that required by the current load demands on the power system. If the reactor temperature needs to be decreased because of lower load demand, the control rods are driven into the core by an amount proportional to the difference between actual and desired temperatures. If a higher reactor temperature is needed for more power, the rods are withdrawn a distance proportional to the difference between the actual and desired temperatures. Although not shown, there are also electronic signals which indicate that the rods have reached the bottom of the core so that the drive can be stopped to prevent damage to the reactor.

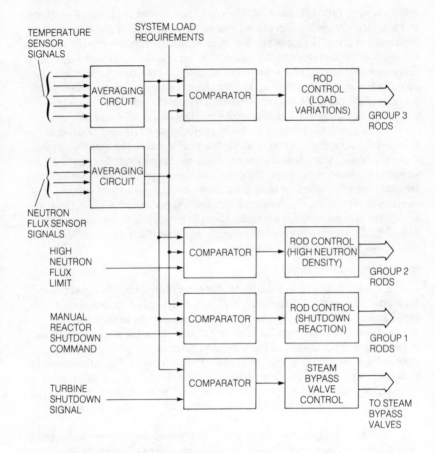

Figure 8-8. *Basic Reactor Electronic Controls*

Computer Control

When the controller is a digital computer as shown in *Figure 8-9*, the temperature and neutron flux inputs are sampled one after another (sequentially) by an analog multiplexer under control of the computer. The multiplexer output is sent to a sample-and-hold circuit which holds the analog value until the A/D converter has passed the resultant digital code to the computer. The digital codes for each sensor are averaged by the processor in the computer and the average is compared to limit values stored in memory. If limits are exceeded, or if a reactor shutdown or turbine shutdown command has been received, the computer will activate the insertion of the shutdown rods, the insertion of the flux control rods, or the steam bypass valve as the situation dictates.

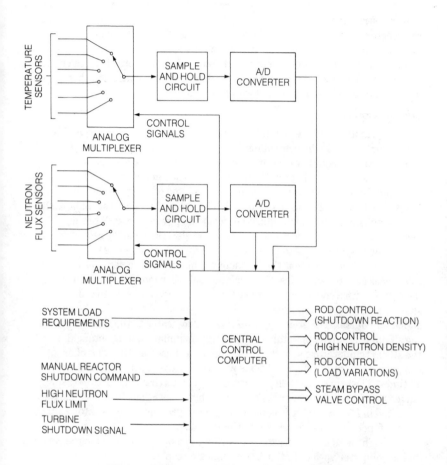

Figure 8-9. Reactor Control Using Computer

If no system limits are exceeded, the computer determines the distance the control rods need to be inserted to bring the reactor power to the desired level. This determination can be done with a look-up table using the current temperature and flux averages, and the current load demand to determine the amount of insertion for the rods. Alternatively, the needed control signals could be computed according to some formula stored in the computer memory. Generally, the computer also monitors the position of the control rods to determine the amount of insertion of each rod or rod group in the core and displays this information. When a rod is completely inserted, an alarm light will be turned on to alert the operators to this condition.

The computer also can make computations on the temperature and power distribution within the reactor, then position rods so that each part of the reactor is producing about the same amount of power to achieve uniform fuel consumption and temperature characteristics. The computer also can compute how fast the fuel is being used and notify operators of the calculated time for replacement of fuel elements, and of boron concentration changes that may be required in a pressurized water reactor.

Turbine Control

Another job the computer can perform is to control the electrical generator frequency by controlling the steam turbine as shown in *Figure 8-10*. The generator frequency control function performed by the computer is the same as described in Chapter 4. The main control element is the electrohydraulic valve which regulates the volume of steam to the turbine. It is activated with pulses as in Chapter 4. The throttle valve is the main valve that establishes the steam required to meet the power demands of the electrical generator, whose load varies as the electrical energy requirements of the power system's customers vary. The governor valve fine tunes the speed of the turbine so that the frequency is maintained to very close tolerances as the load varies. The turbine controller monitors the generator frequency with a speed signal from a tachometer connected to the turbine shaft. This signal is compared to a frequency standard to provide the error signal for control. The steam pressure sensor indicates to the computer that the steam pressure is maintained correctly. A similar input is obtained from the steam temperature sensor. These signals are used by the controller to compare actual operating conditions with the desired operating conditions at all times. The controller then generates the signals that control the steam valves to achieve the proper changes in turbine operation. In addition, as indicated in *Figure 8-10*, the computer also can provide the generator voltage control function that is described in Chapter 4.

The actual control can be according to a program stored in the central digital computer with initiation under operator control and with the opportunity for the operator to input changes manually. Thus, even the start-up of a turbine, how it builds up to operating speed and how the generator is synchronized to the load can be represented in the central digital computer through a program as a sequence of control valve signals versus time. These control signals are sent from the central computer to the turbine electronic controller, which itself may be a computer. The controller causes the valves to activate in a way to meet the programmed objectives at each moment of time. In this way, the start-up (or shut down) of the turbine is performed in an optimum and controlled way by the central computer. The on-line turbine control response to increases or decreases in electrical load also is achieved by following programs stored in computer memory or designed into the controller circuits.

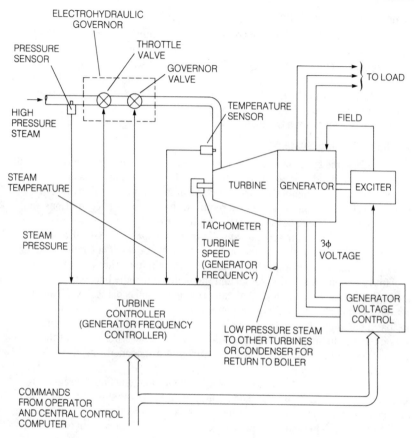

Figure 8-10. *Turbine Control*

The turbine controller also provides a compensation or regulation between momentary unbalances between the reactor power being generated and the demand from the electrical loads. If, for example, reactor power is high and electrical load demand drops, the turbine controller adjusts the throttle valve so that steam is reduced to the turbine. However, the reactor response is relatively slow so the reactor still will be producing more steam than is required. If the pressure within the reactor increases or if the pressure before the throttle valve increases to unacceptably high values, the excess pressure can be relieved by operation of the steam bypass valves. Then the reactor controller can reduce reactor thermal output to match the reduced load requirement. Thus, the turbine controller acts as a buffer between a rapidly changing system (the electrical network) and a slowly changing system (the reactor).

Other Control Functions

A central computer control system also maintains control of other plant systems such as heating and air conditioning, waste material treatment and discharge, and safety systems. The computer system monitors and displays the status of each component of the system, temperature and reactivity profiles of the core, and temperatures and pressures in the steam and turbine generator equipment. The computer is programmed to automatically shut down the plant in case of an emergency or critical failure.

Auxiliary Cooling System

In some types of reactors, loss of coolant flow through the reactor will permit a very rapid increase in core temperatures and vessel pressures to levels that would damage the core structure of fuel elements. To avoid such a serious accident, a control system is required that senses such conditions and provides for emergency cooling of the reactor core.

A basic auxiliary cooling system is shown in *Figure 8-11*. Each pump in this system has a different cooling function so that even if one fails, there are two others that can accomplish the task. The main pumps that circulate the coolant between the reactor vessel and the boiler is usually backed up by another identical set of pumps that can provide normal coolant flow if the first set fails. Similarly, two boilers for generating steam are constructed in parallel so that if one fails to operate correctly, the other can be substituted to produce steam for the turbine and not be shut down. In the case where none of the generators are needed, thus none of the turbines are needed, the steam is vented to the atmosphere.

In *Figure 8-11*, there are two spray loops and one liquid circulation loop used for auxiliary cooling. The high-pressure spray is the first emergency loop used under very critical situations. It introduces cooling water even under conditions of high pressure within the reactor vessel. If there is an emergency, this cooling spray rapidly reduces reactor temperature to below critical levels and to the point where the low pressure spray can maintain the temperature decrease with its cooling action. If the high pressure spray pump should fail, the low pressure emergency coolant pump will turn on. This liquid cooling loop, which acts much like the normal coolant loop to the boiler, but with much cooler return water, would reduce reactor temperature until the low pressure spray can maintain acceptable temperatures in the reactor. During this coolant loop action, valves are controlled to stop the flow to the boiler.

The electronic control system would monitor the operating status of each of the auxiliary cooling loops as well as reactor temperature and reactor vessel pressure. Under manual or emergency command, the control system would then start a controlled or programmed cool-down of the reactor. A different cool-down sequence could be used for each unique situation. For

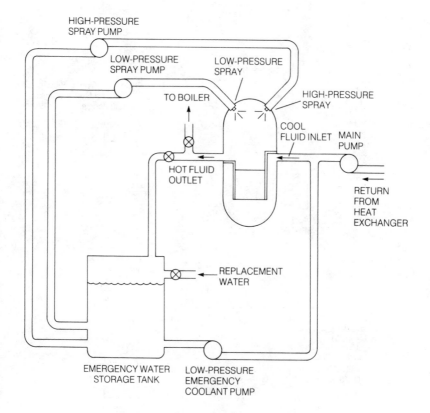

Figure 8-11. *Auxiliary Reactor Cooling System*

example, a uniform temperature change rate should be used for an orderly shut down of the reactor to replace depleted fuel elements, but a very rapid rate would be used for an emergency core cooling requirement.

Alternative Power System

For the reactor, turbine, and cooling system control functions to operate properly, the electronic circuits and computers that make up the control system must have operating power at all times. Thus, there must be several alternative power sources that can be switched onto the control equipment in the event of the failure of one or more of these sources.

A portion of an alternative power system is illustrated in *Figure 8-12*. The operation of this system under normal and emergency situations can be traced by considering the states of the contactors identified by C numbers in *Figure 8-12*. The control electronics, pump motors, and all other electrical equipment (lights, ventilators, etc.) are indicated by the EC blocks.

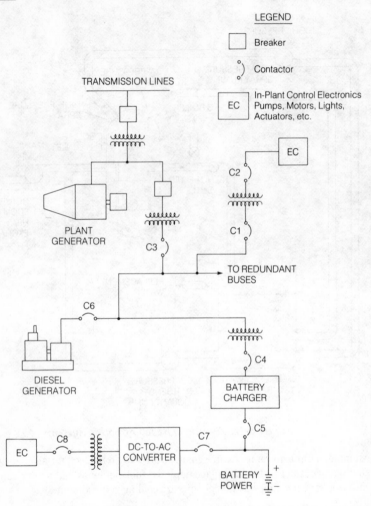

Figure 8-12. *Alternative Power for Control Systems*

Under normal operating conditions, the main plant generator will supply power to the external power transmission lines and, through contactors C1, C2 and C3, to the electrical system of the plant represented by the EC blocks. This power will also keep the emergency batteries charged through closed contactors C3, C4, and C5. Contactors C6, C7 and C8 are open. If the main generator fails or is tripped off-line (as in a black-out), control power must be drawn from either the batteries or the diesel generator. For start-up and normal back-up, the diesel generator would be used by opening contactor

C3 and closing contactor C6. This would maintain the battery charge as well as provide power to the plant electrical system. Contactors C7 and C8 would still be open. If the diesel generator fails as well, then the batteries will supply plant electrical power either directly as direct current power or by using the dc-to-ac converter. In this case, contactors C5, C2, and C6 are all opened and power is delivered from the batteries through contactors C7 and C8.

This system has many alternate paths and the failure of the system due to the failure of a component is very unlikely. However, to make the failure of the plant electrical system impossible (for all practical purposes), the entire system of *Figure 8-12* may be duplicated so that there are two systems throughout the plant. Thus, the control system would have a power back up of two battery packs, two diesel generators, and the main generator. All of these systems would have to fail for plant power to be unavailable.

Radioactivity Monitor and Alarm System

In addition to providing the normal control of the reactor, the turbine-generator combinations, and the alternative systems for reactor cooling and electrical power, the central control system provides other safety services. One of these is to monitor radiation throughout all areas of the plant. The computer constantly samples radiation sensors located in the containment structure, reactor pressure vessel, turbine and generator room, boiler room, control room, fuel building, storage rooms and in any other critical areas of the plant. If the sensors indicate radiation levels above a preset limit that is stored in the computer, alarms will be sounded in the control room and in the area affected. This has the immediate effect of warning personnel to clear the area for their own safety. Also, it usually indicates an operational problem that if continued, may lead to a plant emergency or damage to some of the plant equipment. This early warning of problem areas provides time to take corrective action before equipment is damaged or radiation levels increase to dangerous levels.

The computer also monitors liquid levels in the reactor vessel, boilers and coolant loop to detect early problems in these areas. If a low liquid level is detected, it may indicate a pipe rupture or vessel rupture. This would require immediate attention and possibly may cause a plant shut-down.

As can be seen from the discussion in this chapter, the basic control functions for a nuclear power plant divide into three areas: normal operation and control of the plant for power generation; control of alternative systems to ensure safe operation of the plant during a malfunction that may cause an emergency; and monitoring plant conditions and sounding alarms when necessary. The total control system is complex and requires fast processing of data that only can be handled effectively by a large central computer. In addition, in many installations, small satellite control computers also may be required.

The combination of parallel systems, computer control, and emergency electrical power for the control elements and control center ensures that a nuclear plant may be safely operated, even in a populated environment. Other factors such as operation economics, fuel availability, waste disposal, and environmental impact have not been covered in this book since the main concern of this book is electronic control and the impact of electronics in implementing the control functions required.

WHAT HAVE WE LEARNED?

1. Nuclear energy using fission reactions is a safe and viable way of generating electrical power at the present time.
2. Nuclear fusion power is in the future. If commercially feasible, it is projected that fusion power plants could meet the world's energy needs for an inconceivable period of time (billions of years).
3. The fission reaction starts with U^{235} or Pu^{239} being bombarded by a neutron. The atom splits into two smaller atoms and two or more additional neutrons. The reaction is controlled by control rods or moderator coolant in the reactor absorbing the correct number of neutrons so the chain reaction does not avalanche beyond a certain level.
4. One job the electronic control system must perform is to continually adjust the position of the control rods to match the reactor power generation to the system load.
5. The fission reaction produces reactor thermal energy which produces steam. The steam drives turbines which drives generators to generate electrical energy.
6. Reactors are cooled by water, gas, or a liquid metal. The coolant must be circulated continually to keep the reactor temperature within safe limits and to provide a method for extracting the thermal energy generated by the reactor.
7. The electronic control system must detect improper reactor temperatures and activate alternate cooling systems when temperatures exceed limits.
8. Electronic control systems control generator voltage and generator frequency as necessary.
9. Electronic control systems monitor radioactivity levels and the status of all equipment to detect unusual operating conditions. If emergency conditions exist, the control system sounds appropriate alarms and identifies the unusual conditions for the operators.
10. The nuclear power plant is an excellent example of how the power of computer control systems can be used to provide safe and economical operation of even the most complex of energy systems.

Quiz for Chapter 8

1. In a slow fission reactor, the purpose of the moderator is to:
   a. control the generator frequency.
   b. slow down neutrons.
   c. provide cooling for the turbine.
   d. reduce fuel consumption.

2. In a fission reaction, about what percentage of the reaction energy shows up as kinetic energy of particles?
   a. 5
   b. 10
   c. 20
   d. 80
   e. 85

3. In a fast breeder reactor:
   a. fast neutrons are used in producing the reaction.
   b. new fuel is generated from the fission of old fuel.
   c. control rods are not needed.
   d. all of the above.
   e. a and b above.

4. The total number of fuel rods in a fission reactor is typically:
   a. 40
   b. 200
   c. 1,000
   d. 8,000 or more

5. Control rods are used in a reactor to:
   a. absorb neutrons to slow down reaction.
   b. shut down the reactor in emergency situations.
   c. reduce the level of temperature in a reactor.
   d. reduce the number of neutrons produced in the reactor.
   e. all of the above.
   f. a and b above.

6. The coolant in a fast breeder reactor is:
   a. sodium.
   b. water.
   c. helium.
   d. lithium.

7. The main effect of a catastrophic nuclear plant accident would be:
   a. a nuclear explosion.
   b. a chemical explosion.
   c. release of radioactive material into the environment.
   d. none of the above.

8. The coolant flow in a reactor vessel is:
   a. first around the periphery of the core.
   b. first through the center of the core.
   c. simultaneously around and through the core.

9. A heat exchanger type steam boiler is not absolutely necessary in a:
   a. pressurized water reactor.
   b. boiling water reactor.
   c. gas cooled reactor.
   d. fast breeder reactor.

10. The coolant flow paths through the core are largest in a:
    a. pressurized water reactor.
    b. boiling water reactor.
    c. gas cooled reactor.
    d. breeder reactor.

11. Steam produced in a gas cooled reactor is typically how many degrees Fahrenheit?
    a. 500
    b. 700
    c. 1,000
    d. 1,500

12. The steam temperature in a liquid sodium reactor is about how many degrees Fahrenheit?
    a. 800
    b. 1,000
    c. 1,500
    d. 2,000

13. As fission fuel is consumed in a reactor, the control rods must be:
    a. lowered further into the core.
    b. left in their same position.
    c. raised out of the core.

14. Temperature within the reactor is monitored by using:
  a. thermocouples.
  b. thermistors.
  c. neutron detectors.
  d. radiation detectors.

15. The control system in a fission plant monitors:
  a. reactor neutron flux.
  b. reactor temperature.
  c. containment structure neutron flux.
  d. radiation levels around the plant.
  e. all of the above.
  f. a, b, and c above.
  g. a, b, and d above.

16. In a steam turbine that generates electrical power, the throttle and governor adjust the:
  a. electrical voltage amplitude.
  b. exciter voltage.
  c. frequency of the ac power.
  d. steam pressure delivered to the turbine.
  e. all of the above.
  f. a and b above.
  g. c and d above.

17. The auxiliary diesel power plant in a nuclear plant:
  a. provides emergency power to the plant in case of a main generator failure.
  b. provides start-up electrical power.
  c. provides charging current to the battery bank.
  d. all of the above.

18. The auxiliary cooling system is used to provide:
  a. cooling to the control room and work areas.
  b. cooling to the containment building.
  c. cooling to the reactor vessel during normal operation.
  d. system cooling under emergency situations.

19. If all functions of the auxiliary cooling system are working normally, the initial cooling of a overheated reactor is by the:
  a. high-pressure spray.
  b. low-pressure spray.
  c. circulating coolant pump.
  d. all of the above.

20. Radioactivity is monitored:
  a. throughout the plant.
  b. only near the reactor vessel.
  c. only in the fuel storage area.
  d. only in the containment building.

How to Use Programmable Energy Controllers

ABOUT THIS CHAPTER

Almost all of the early energy control systems used only electromechanical components such as valves, relays, thermostats, and motors. As electronic technology provided inexpensive functional elements such as amplifiers, power switching, and digital operations (counting, switching, decoding, and analog-to-digital conversion), the electromechanical devices were driven by electronic control systems. At first, these control systems used all analog techniques, but later they used specially designed digital control systems. In the past few years, almost all new energy control systems have been implemented using some form of programmable digital control system. This chapter will examine more closely the reason for this trend to programmable control systems and how these systems are designed. A specific industrial energy control system will be discussed as an example.

WHAT IS A PROGRAMMABLE CONTROL SYSTEM?

The concept and structure of a programmable control system have been presented in various forms throughout this book, beginning with the general features in Chapter 3. To review these concepts, the basic structure of a programmable control system is shown in *Figure 9-1*.

By now, the functions shown in *Figure 9-1* should be familiar. The inputs are of two types: (1) human operator commands via switches, controls and keyboards, and (2) system state conditions such as temperature, speed, and power consumption via sensors. The outputs also are of two types: (1) status reports to human operators via displays and alarms, and (2) action commands to actuators, motors, heaters, and so on.

The central element of the control system is the processor which determines how each part of the system is to behave and when any action is to take place. The processor performs this central control function under the direction of the control program—the sequence of instructions stored in the system memory. Also stored in system memory are the data that are received from the input devices, the results of computation and other processor operations, and the control codes that are to be sent to the output devices. All of these peripheral units go into action when the processor addresses them under control of the program instructions.

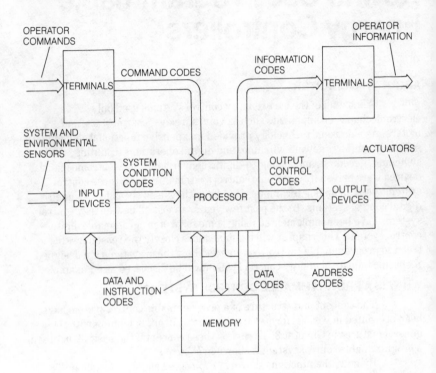

Figure 9-1. *Components of Programmable Control Systems*

The processor may be a single integrated circuit, called a microprocessor, or it may be a large piece of electronic equipment specifically designed for use in a control system application. In fact, the form and size of the functional elements of *Figure 9-1* depend on the complexity of the control task. The control of a few electrical motors or an internal combustion engine usually can be handled by a single integrated circuit microprocessor with supporting integrated circuit memory, and input and output devices interconnected on one or more printed circuit boards. The control of a large-scale system such as a nuclear reactor or other power plant involves the use of large central computer facilities with many small microcomputers spread out over a large area. Each microcomputer supports some individual input, output or computing task. However, both small-scale and large-scale systems need a programmable control system.

WHAT ARE THE ADVANTAGES OF A PROGRAMMABLE CONTROL SYSTEM?

Hardware Advantages

From a hardware design point of view, the advantage of the programmable control system over a hard-wired (fixed operation) control system is that the interconnections of the hardware are the same for all systems. This makes the initial system design and construction much simpler since the designer just selects the processor module and memory components needed, connects the appropriate input and output terminal elements, and provides the input sensor and output control devices needed. Thus, a designer with very little special training can develop control systems using standard input, output, processor, and memory components. Also, the designer can expand or modify system operation with very little additional design effort or cost because the system is easily expanded by adding more memory or input and output elements as needed.

In order for this advantage of the programmable approach to be realized, system components must be available that are designed to provide the common input, output, processor, and memory functions that are needed by all such systems and these components must be easily interconnected. We'll discuss a group of industrial control systems that meet these requirements a little later, but for now, let's look at some other advantages.

Software Advantages

Another advantage of a programmable control system is related to the very fact that the system is programmable; that is, its operation can be changed by simply changing the system program—the set of instructions that guides the system through the step-by-step sequences of operations as it performs a task. Because of this, a given system structure can satisfy many control system requirements. The system behavior is tailored to a specific application by an appropriate computer program. If the system operation is to be expanded, or if the control decisions are to be more complex, or if system operation is to be modified, only the program needs to be changed. (Of course, if new inputs or outputs are required, the necessary input or output hardware devices must be added.)

In order for the full advantage of the programmable approach to be realized, the programming of the system (called developing software) must be made as simple as possible. Humans must communicate their thoughts and ideas to the digital system by giving instructions that digital systems understand. This is done by programming in a computer language. Assembly language is one of these. While an experienced programmer may be able to use assembly language to develop programs, less experienced programmers need a simple, but powerful, language that is directed to solving their specific problem. This will permit them to write programs quickly, accurately, and at low cost. One such language is the BASIC language which can be easily learned and applied to control system programming. This is the language used in many home and small-business computers. Another language is the one used in the TI PM550 programmable control systems. This language is directly related to the control problem; therefore, if the designer can describe the control system in circuit form, he can readily convert this description into program form. The ease with which the control system requirements can be described both in hardware form (physical units) and in software form (program) will be evident when some repesentative problems are considered a little later.

WHAT ARE SOME TYPICAL PROGRAMMABLE CONTROL SYSTEM COMPONENTS?

The simplest approach to designing a specialized programmable control system for use in an application of moderate or above complexity is to use "off-the-shelf" components that have been designed specifically for control systems. An example of systems manufactured by a number of companies is the line of industrial programmable controller systems manufactured by Texas Instruments Incorporated. This family of industrial control systems provides all of the functions of *Figure 9-1* in an easily interconnected and programmed set of units. These units can handle a control task from something as simple as a home energy system to a system as complex as a modern industrial factory. Since the units are easily interconnected, the actual design of the system is simply a matter of selecting the right module for each system input, output, memory, or processor task and interconnecting them to form the needed system. Similarly, the programming of the resulting system has been simplified so that developing and changing the control program is a simple and low-cost task.

The Series 500 family consists of the Model 510, 520, 530, and PM550 programmable controller systems. These systems can handle from 12 inputs and 8 outputs to 1,023 inputs and outputs. The latest technology in programming, interface, ease of use, reliability and economy is incorporated in these systems. They have processing built into the I/O modules, distributed I/O, self-diagnostics, and networking for easy expansion.

A brief description of the simplest of the Series 500 programmable controller systems, the Model 510, and of the full-range program master 550 (PM550) system will give an indication of the broad scope of such systems.

Model 510

The Model 510 programmable controller system consists of the programmable controller and its associated programmer as shown in *Figure 9-2*. It is a sequential controller that can accept 12 inputs and provide 8 outputs. The inputs are designed to detect the presence or absence of nominal 120 VAC or nominal 24 VDC signals without additional I/O interfacing. Inputs can be from push-button switch contacts, limit switches, pressure switches, etc. The outputs, which are TRIAC controlled, can supply up to 2 amperes at 120 VAC to drive solenoid valves, motor starters, indicators, etc.

The programmable controller has a processor, read-write memory, and input and output circuits so that it meets all the requirements of *Figure 9-1*.

The programmer has a calculator keyboard and display that allows control programs to be input to the programmable controller. It also allows the operator to check and edit progams, display the contents of storage locations that contain data or status information, permanently store programs, and execute programs entered into the system.

By a simple sequence of keystrokes, the program can be entered directly into the programmable controller. With inputs and outputs properly in place, the program can be executed to exercise the system and complete the task.

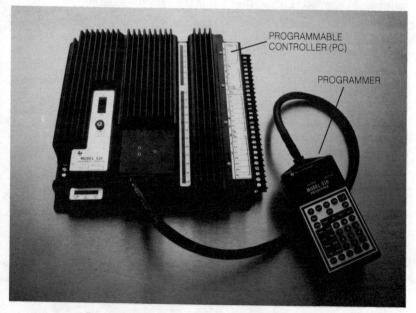

Figure 9-2. Model 510 Programmable Controller

PM550

The PM550 system is shown in *Figures 9-3* and *9-4*. It consists of a Central Control Unit (CCU), a Timer/Counter Access Module (TCAM), a Loop Access Module (LAM), 6MT Input/Output modules for ac and dc ON-OFF type signals, 7MT Input/Output modules for analog signals, an optional I/O Expander Module, a power supply and two types of terminals. The terminal options include a Read-Write Programmer (*Figure 9-4a*) that resembles a desktop calculator, and a Video Programming Unit (VPU) (*Figure 9-4b*) that has a CRT and a typewriter keyboard. The optional Computer Interface Module (*Figure 9-4c*) can be placed in the CCU to provide communication with a central computer. The functional interconnection of the components is shown in *Figure 9-5*.

Central Control Unit

The Central Control Unit consists of two microprocessors along with associated memory, timers, and input and output circuits to interface to the I/O units. The processors perform operations on instructions and data codes that are 16-bit binary codes. A portion of the memory is devoted to the program storage, a portion is devoted to system variable data, and a portion is devoted to the storage of system constants for use in system calculations and decision making. The CCU may contain a Computer Interface Module that provides control and communication from a central computer (sometimes called a host computer). Thus, the CCU in the PM550 system may be controlled by a central computer or it can be a separate and self-contained independent computer control system.

For operator use, the CCU provides interface to commercially available terminals or printers through two serial communications lines (called ports) with data rates of 300 or 1200 bits per second (300 or 1200 baud in computer terminology). In addition, the CCU has I/O interface circuits to transfer information to 64 analog inputs or outputs through 7MT modules and up to 256 inputs and outputs through 6MT modules. A port provides an interface to the LAM and TCAM modules so that initial values and system adjustments can be input into the system. Any given module can be connected easily to the CCU, for it is just a matter of connecting the proper cable between the CCU and the external module. The TCAMs and LAMs can be located up to 1,000 feet from the CCU.

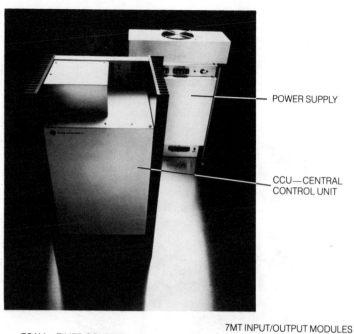

POWER SUPPLY

CCU—CENTRAL
CONTROL UNIT

TCAM—TIMER/COUNTER
ACCESS MODULE

LAM—LOOP ACCESS
MODULE

7MT INPUT/OUTPUT MODULES

6MT INPUT/OUTPUT MODULES

I/O EXPANDER

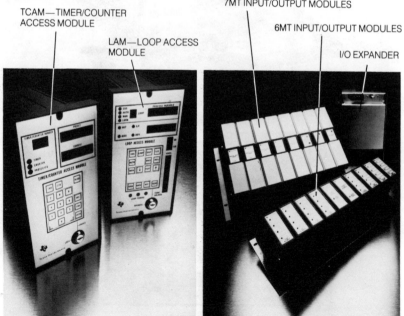

Figure 9-3. PM550 System Components

a. Read/Write Programmer

b. VPU—Video Programming Unit

c. Computer Interface Module

Figure 9-4. PM550 System Terminals

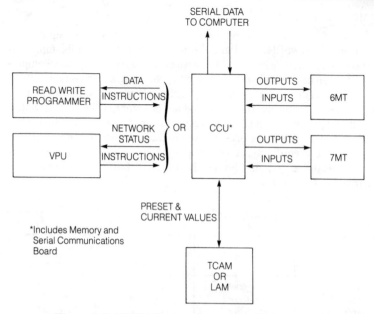

Figure 9-5. PM550 System Component Interconnection

TCAM and LAM

The TCAMs and LAMs have a keyboard and LED (light-emitting diode) display for numbers and letters. They contain a microprocessor so that they act as more than just an input/output terminal for the CCU. The TCAM allows the operator to monitor and adjust values of the timers and counters in the CCU that are used by the system program. A counter is a device that starts counting from zero, counts up to a preset count, and then notifies the CCU that the count has been reached. A timer starts out at a preset value and counts down to zero to represent an interval of time. When the timer reaches zero, it notifies the CCU. In applications, the TCAM can be used to set timers and counters to time system events and to count the number of times certain things happen as the system operates. With the LAM, the operator is able to adjust parameters of particular control loops in the system.

Operator Terminals

Both types of operator terminals, the Read-Write Programmer and the VPU, allow operators to enter system programs into the CCU memory, test the operation of the system, start the system in its program execution mode, and monitor the status of system operating conditions. The Read-Write Programmer has a keypad for input and an LED display for output. The VPU receives operator inputs from the keyboard and outputs messages and drawings of system control circuits on a CRT to provide an interactive, user-friendly communication terminal.

6MT Modules

The 6MT modules outputs can switch either ac or dc voltages. Nominal ac voltages of 24, 120 and 240 supplying from tens of milliamperes to 3 amperes and dc voltages from 4 to 160 with currents from tens of milliamperes to 1 ampere can be controlled. These should provide all of the voltage combinations needed to control motors, lights, relays, and other common power elements. Similarly, the input modules can monitor these same voltage levels, drawing a maximum of 30 milliamperes from the monitored line. The input module determines the presence or absence of power on a given line and signals the CCU accordingly. A separate rack is provided for interconnecting these modules to the system. The specifications for the 6MT modules are summarized in *Table 9-1*.

Table 9-1. 6MT Module Specifications

Number	Type	Rating	
		Voltage	Current
6MT11-A05L	*AC Input	85-132 Vac	30 mA max
6MT11-E05L	*AC Input	17-28 Vac	28 mA max
6MT11-B05L	*AC Input	170-260 Vac	30 mA max
6MT12-40AL	*AC Output	85-132 Vac	2A
6MT12-40BL	*AC Output	170-260 Vac	2A
6MT12-40EL	*AC Output	17-28 Vac	3A max
6MT13-D05L	DC Input	4-28 Vdc	10 mA max
6MT13-G05L	DC Input	40-160 Vdc	10 mA max
6MT14-40CL	DC Output	10-28 Vdc	1A
6MT14-40DL	DC Output	5-28 Vdc	0.1A
6MT14-40GL	DC Output	40-160 Vdc	0.5A

*47-63 Hz

7MT Modules

Some of the 7MT modules accept analog inputs and perform A/D conversion to provide a serial digital output to the CCU. Others accept serial digital inputs from the CCU and perform D/A conversion to provide analog outputs. Other modules accept parallel digital signal inputs and provide parallel digital outputs. A special purpose thermocouple module converts a thermocouple output to digital equivalent codes. This is particularly useful in heating and cooling system control applications. Again, a separate rack is available for easy interconnection to the system. *Table 9-2* lists the 7MT module types.

***Table 9-2.** 7MT Module Specifications*

Number	Type	Range	Accuracy		Resolution
			Voltage	**Current**	
7MT-100	Analog Input	0-5.12 V 0-20.48 mA	0.1%	1%	12 Bits
7MT-200	Analog Output	0-10.24 V 0-20.48 mA	0.42%	2%	10 Bits
7MT-300	Digital Parallel Input	4.75-5.25 VDC 10-28 VDC	—	—	—
7MT-400	Digital Parallel Output	4.75-5.25 VDC	—	—	—
7MT-500	Thermocouple Input	0-50 mVDC	—	—	12 Bits

I/O Expander

The I/O Expander module increases the 6MT I/O capacity of the CCU from 96 inputs and/or outputs to 256 inputs/outputs.

Power Supply Module

The Power Supply module provides + 5.1, –5, + 12, –12, and + 9.1 volts to the CCU. It also can supply ± 12 and + 5.1 volts to each of two 7MT mounting racks. It provides + 9.1 volt power to two LAMs and/or TCAMs. The 6MT I/O modules and racks provide their own power, as do the operator terminals.

HOW ARE PROGRAMMABLE CONTROL SYSTEMS DESIGNED?

The design of a programmable control system has two separate, but related tasks. One is the selection and interconnection of the hardware—the physical components. The other is the development of the software—the programs for the system. Let's examine these tasks for specific applications.

Basic Control Circuit

The simplest control situation is shown in *Figure 9-6a*. This system or portion of a system is nothing more than a switch that controls a motor. *Figure 9-6b* shows this circuit in the form usually used in industrial control diagrams. This form is called a ladder diagram because the diagram resembles a ladder with main power on the vertical side rails and circuit branches forming the rungs. The component symbols used in these diagrams are different from those used on an electronic schematic diagram. For example, normally-open switch contacts are represented by two parallel lines as shown in *Figure 9-6b*. Normally-closed switch contacts are represented by two parallel lines crossed by a diagonal line. In *Figure 9-6b*, the switch has been named X9 (X9 is chosen to correspond to the Model 510 input terminal used). The motor has been named Y1 and is represented by a circle. The power lines are represented by the outside pair of vertical lines.

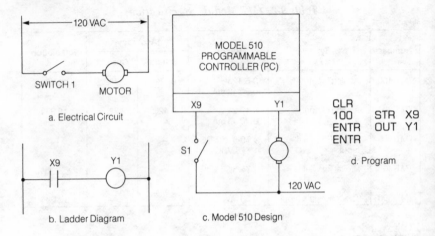

Figure 9-6. *Single Input/Single Output System*

The Model 510 hardware required includes an input to sense the switch condition and an output connected to the motor. Both are provided by the Programmable Controller (PC) as shown in *Figure 9-6c*.

The software program that represents the ladder structure of *Figure 9-6b* is shown in *Figure 9-6d*. The existence of the X9 contacts is indicated by the STR X9 instruction and the existence of the motor is indicated by the OUT Y1 instruction. The CLR and ENTR instructions are standard procedure instructions that clear the display and tell the CCU to accept the instruction. The final ENTR indicates the end of the program. These will be included in all examples. The 100 before the STR X9 instruction is the starting location for the program in memory. The program instructions shown in *Figure 9-6d*, as well as those used in figures that follow, are shown in the same form as they would be input into the Model 510 Programmer.

Logical Circuits

Slightly more complicated circuits are shown in *Figures 9-7* and *9-8* in a similar fashion. *Figure 9-7* shows two series-connected switches controlling a motor. The series-connected switches function as an AND gate, as discussed in Chapter 3, since both S1 (switch 1) AND S2 (switch 2) have to be in the true or closed state for the motor to operate. Similarly, the parallel-connected switches of *Figure 9-8* provide a logical OR gate function, as discussed in Chapter 3, since the closure of either S1 (switch 1) OR S2 (switch 2) will activate the motor. The electrical schematics are shown in *Figures 9-7a* and *9-8a*. The corresponding ladder diagrams are shown in *Figures 9-7b* and *9-8b*. *Figures 9-7c* and *9-8c* show the simple hardware design using the Model 510. The corresponding program statements (software) are shown in *Figures 9-7d* and *9-8d*. Notice the use of the AND instruction in *Figure 9-7d* and the OR instruction in *Figure 9-8d*.

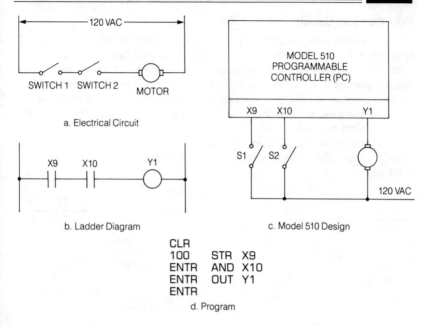

Figure 9-7. Two Series Inputs/One Output System

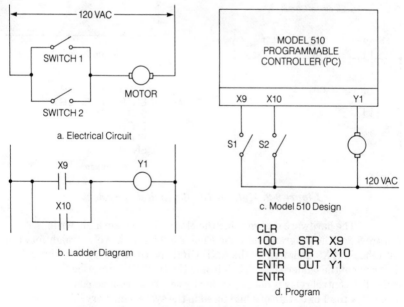

Figure 9-8. Parallel Inputs/Single Output System

More Complex Circuit

A more complex circuit is shown in *Figure 9-9*. In this system, the motor operation is controlled by a switch and a relay contact in a series (AND) connection, with the relay contact closure controlled by another switch that controls current flow to the relay coil. The coil of the relay is shown as a circle with the notation of CR (for control relay) while the contacts of the relay are shown as a switch, but with the same CR notation. The circuit of *Figure 9-9a* is represented in *Figure 9-9b* in ladder diagram form with the switch contacts (X9) and relay contacts (CR1) in series with the power element (Y1). This branch is in parallel with the relay control switch (X10) and the relay coil (CR1 again).

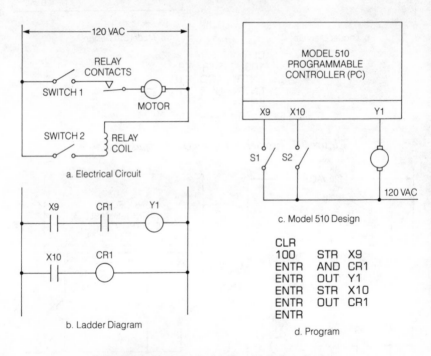

Figure 9-9. Multiple Input with Relay System

The hardware design using the Model 510 system is shown in *Figure 9-9c*. The program, shown in *Figure 9-9d*, is relatively straightforward with the STR X9, followed by the AND CR1, and the OUT Y1 describing the first rung of the ladder. The STR X10 and the OUT CR1 describe the second rung. The control relay is not an actual physical relay connected to the Model 510, but is the 1 or 0 state of a bit stored in the system memory. The PC checks the state of the bit to see if power is to be delivered to the motor or not.

Simple Control System

The circuits of *Figures 9-6* through *9-9* are the basic circuits that are used in various combinations to design complicated control systems. By learning how these circuits work and are diagrammed and programmed, almost any system can be designed and programmed. *Figure 9-10a* provides an example of a system that combines several of the circuits of *Figures 9-6* through *9-9*. This is the control system for a small-scale electrical furnace with a single-phase fan motor of the type used in a home heating system. The fan motor control can be handled directly by an output from a Model 510 PC, but the 10-kilowatt electrical heater power requirement is too great for direct control by a Model 510. The heater power must be controlled by a power contactor that is controlled by a PC output.

A master relay, CR2, activates the system. It is energized with the start switch, S3, and de-energized with the stop switch, S2. It has contacts, CR2, that keep the relay energized after the start push-button switch is released. It has contacts in the fan motor relay circuit and the heater contactor circuit.

The fan motor will receive power if its branch circuit breaker, S1, is on and if the control relay contacts, CR1, are closed. The control relay, CR1, will be energized if the master relay contacts, CR2, are closed; if the fan motor is not in an overload condition; and if the fan control contacts, CR3, are closed or the SV switch is closed to make the fan run continuously. The fan control relay, CR3, is energized when the room thermostat demands heat and the duct temperature thermostat, STL, contacts are closed because a minimum temperature has been reached in the duct. The heater contactor that applies power to the heater will be energized if the heater control contacts, CR4, are closed and the master relay contacts, CR2, are closed. The heater control relay, CR4, will be energized when the system is manually placed in the heat mode with switch, SM; when the room thermostat, ST, demands heat; and when the temperature of the duct is not high enough to open the thermostatic switch STH. Note that the power circuits operate from 120 VAC and the control circuits operate from 24 VDC. The heater operates from 240 VAC instead of 120 VAC to produce heat at a lower current. The 240 VAC is applied to the heater by the contactor contacts.

The corresponding ladder diagram is shown in *Figure 9-11a* where the circuit breakers, push-button switches, thermostatic switches and manual switches are indicated as input contacts. X9 through X13 are used for the ac rungs and X15 through X18 are used for dc rungs. (Note that the room thermostat, ST, is shown twice although there is only one physically.) The fan motor, master, fan control and heater control relays are indicated as CR1 through CR4, respectively. The fan motor output is indicated by Y1 and the heater contactor by Y2.

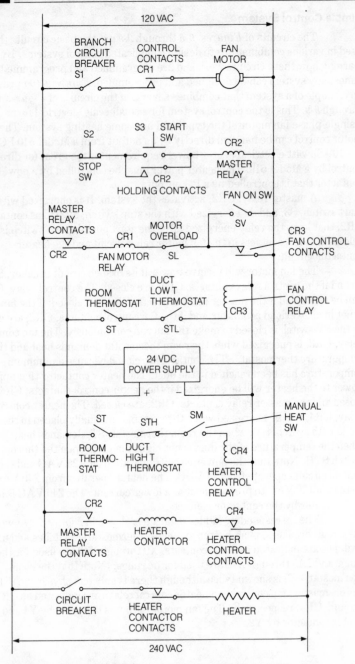

Figure 9-10. Electric Furnace System Electrical Circuit

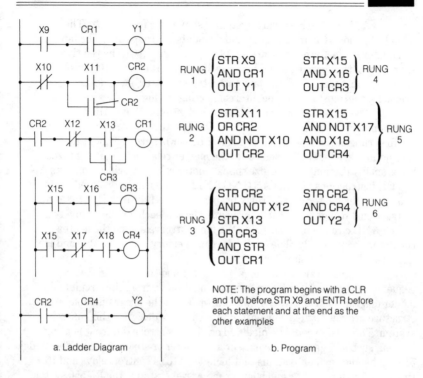

a. Ladder Diagram

b. Program

RUNG 1
STR X9
AND CR1
OUT Y1

RUNG 2
STR X11
OR CR2
AND NOT X10
OUT CR2

RUNG 3
STR CR2
AND NOT X12
STR X13
OR CR3
AND STR
OUT CR1

RUNG 4
STR X15
AND X16
OUT CR3

RUNG 5
STR X15
AND NOT X17
AND X18
OUT CR4

RUNG 6
STR CR2
AND CR4
OUT Y2

NOTE: The program begins with a CLR
and 100 before STR X9 and ENTR before
each statement and at the end as the
other examples

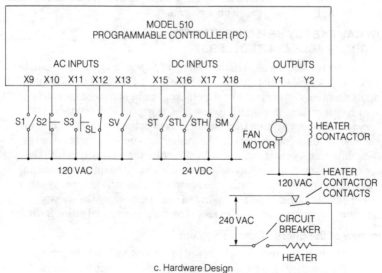

c. Hardware Design

Figure 9-11. Electric Furnace System Using Programmable Controller

A Model 510 hardware system is shown in *Figure 9-11c*. The Model 510 allows the mixing of ac and dc inputs in groups of 6. The fan motor and heater contactor outputs are supplied from 120 VAC. The relative simplicity of the system should be quite apparent. It essentially consists of the programmable controller, the fan motor, the contactor, switches, circuit breakers, thermostats and the interconnecting wiring.

The program that would be entered into the Model 510 with the Programmer is shown in *Figure 9-11b*. The first three instructions describe the first rung of the ladder, the fan motor power branch. The next four instructions are for the second rung, the master relay power. Rung three takes six instructions to energize the fan motor relay branch. It contains AND and OR instructions and the AND NOT X12 for the normally closed contacts. Rung 5 for the heater control relay branch is an AND branch that takes four instructions. Rungs 4 and 6 use three instructions each for the simple two-switch AND circuits for energizing the fan control relay and the heater contactor, respectively. The CLR, starting memory location of 100 and ENTR have been left out for simplicity.

The hardware wiring of *Figure 9-11c* and the entire software sequence of *Figure 9-11b* follow quickly and directly from the circuit and ladder diagrams of *Figures 9-10* and *9-11a*. Thus, the programmable structure provides a very low-cost approach to the design of this control system. This design could be modified easily to control a different heating system, such as a gas-fired furnace or a hot water or steam system. The Model 510 can handle smaller systems that include up to 64 control relays and 16 timers and counters. For much larger industrial systems, the PM550 system must be used. Let's look at such an application.

HOW CAN ENERGY BE MANAGED WITH PROGRAMMABLE CONTROLLERS?

The techniques used in the system of *Figure 9-10* can be expanded to a large scale. A system that justifies the use of the PM550 in a distributed computer control system is the energy management of a large industrial plant. One such system that has been implemented using the PM550 system is the energy management system that was first used in the semiconductor plant of Texas Instruments Incorporated. The system was designed and tested at several different levels of control to demonstrate the ease with which the programmable control system could be expanded and adapted to changing system requirements. Currently, the control system is used in many other plants of Texas Instruments Incorporated and is managing the energy utilization in over 8 million square feet of manufacturing and office facilities.

Overview of the Energy Control System

The basic control areas involved in the system block diagram are shown in *Figure 9-12*. Each control area is handled by an independent PM550 system which can be programmed directly with a Read-Write Programmer or VPU, or it can be programmed from the central control and monitor computer.

In this installation, the central computer is a Texas Instruments TM990. Status and summary information on system operation can be obtained from VPUs or printers attached to individual PM550 stations or from the CRT terminal or printer attached to the central control computer. The failure of any given PM550 will not affect the rest of the system, so that energy management and savings can continue for the other areas. Let's look at the operation of the various PM550s.

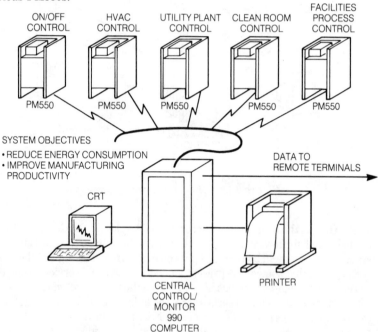

Figure 9-12. Energy Management System

ON/OFF Control System

In *Figure 9-13*, the On/Off Control System turns off equipment when it is not in use and turns it back on when it is needed. This system can turn equipment on or off according to a programmed schedule. It may be a schedule based on the time of day, or on temperature, or on temperature set-back or set-up, or on some duty cycle or sequencing plan. The system action may be as a result of an operator request or it may be on the basis of whether the room lights are on or off. To accomplish this, the room temperature is monitored by a temperature sensor, and an air handler or blower for the area is controlled to supply the heated or cooled air to control the temperature as necessary. The lights are monitored and controlled. A timer measures elapsed time and it can notify the PM550 CCU that equipment or service to a space can be turned off because it hasn't been used for a specified time. A printer keeps a record of the date, time, location and identification of any alarm condition that occurs.

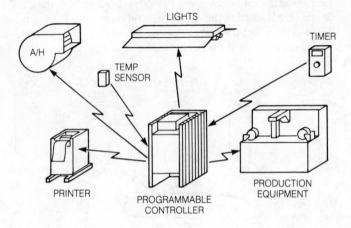

Figure 9-13. *ON/OFF Control System*

Here is the basic design approach used by the On/Off Control System. Equipment and air flow remain off or at very low standby levels until an operator demands them by turning lights on in the area. This signals the control system that someone is present and normal levels of service should be restored. If a time-of-service has been preset in the timer, the timer starts its countdown. When the count reaches zero, the lights are blinked on and off to warn that air flow, lights, and equipment service is about to be reduced. If the operator does not request additional time, the air flow, lights, and equipment are reduced to their standby levels. When the timer is activated, either by the preprogrammed schedule or by the operator providing a new request for lights and room use, the system is turned back on to active levels by the PM550 controller.

HVAC Control System

The main central heating, ventilation, and air-conditioning (HVAC) system is controlled by a separate PM550 system as shown in *Figure 9-12*. A subsystem of the HVAC system controls air flow in the ducts. *Figure 9-14* shows how this is implemented using a PM550. The main purpose is to maintain the airflow, room temperature and room pressure between acceptable limits.

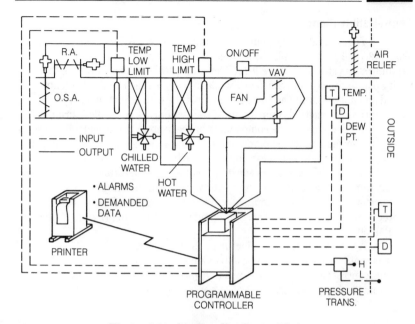

Figure 9-14. *Air Handler Control System*

The PM550 is programmed to provide space temperature deadband control. This means that air is cooled if it goes above 76°F or heated if it goes below 70°F (or any other limits the operator wishes to set); thus, a deadband exists for the temperature range between 70°F and 76°F. The air handler subsystem controls the dampers, fan motors, and heat exchangers to accomplish this. For example, inputs from sensors measuring duct temperatures, inside and outside air temperature, inside and outside dew point, and room air pressure are fed into 6MT and 7MT input modules which feed the information to the PM550. As a result, the PM550 controls the following through 6MT or 7MT output modules:

1. The flow of chilled water and hot water to their respective heat exchangers in the ducts;
2. The mixture of return air and outside air by positioning the R.A. and O.S.A. dampers;
3. The air flow to branch ducts by switching the duct fan motor on or off or by positioning the duct variable air volume (VAV) dampers;
4. The room air pressure by controlling the air relief exhaust dampers to the outside.

Besides these main control loops, the PM550 system can compute energy requirements, monitor space and energy utilization, and inform the system operator of the status of these variables so that waste and inefficiencies are held to a minimum.

Central Utility Plant

The central utility plant subsystem of the HVAC system is shown in *Figure 9-15*. This utility plant provides hot water and chilled water to the air handling subsystem of *Figure 9-14*. The controller's task is to operate the utility plant at maximum efficiency while it provides the required amounts of chilled and hot water at the correct temperature with minimum energy consumption. The actual components of the system are controlled through 6MT and 7MT modules. The components of the system being controlled are the cooling tower fan and water pump, the chilled water and hot water pumps, the chiller inlet vane and the bypass valves at the boiler, chiller, and cooling tower. The controller monitors the dew point and temperature of the outside air, the temperature of the cooling tower water, and the temperature and pressure of the chilled water supply and hot water supply. The control strategy for the operation of these components is stored in program form in the PM550.

A semiconductor manufacturing facility has special HVAC requirements such as clean rooms and exhaust air systems. Additional PM550 systems control these areas as shown in *Figure 9-12*, as well as provide control of manufacturing processes.

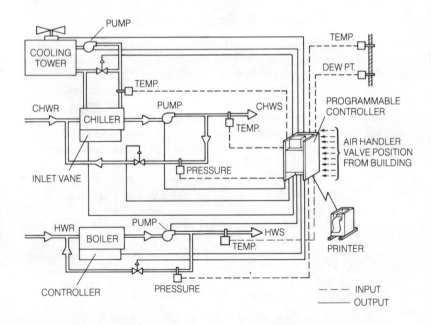

Figure 9-15. *Central Utility Plant Control System*

Overall System

A somewhat more detailed system diagram of *Figure 9-16* shows how the TM990 central computer is linked to the PM550 programmable controllers to form the complete energy management system indicated in *Figure 9-12*. The 6MT and 7MT I/O modules are not shown, but are assumed to be in place.

The central utility plant provides chilled and hot water to the central fan and duct unit to provide a large volume of air at the correct general use temperature. This temperature is modified by an air handler for a particular space by controlling the flow of chilled water and hot water to the dual duct heat exchangers and controlling the flow of hot and cold air from these ducts to the use space with the air flow dampers. All the cooling and heating requirements of the entire facility are summed by the TM990 computer to determine the operation required from the central utility plant cooling tower, boiler and support equipment.

The compressed air for the manufacturing areas and special hot water heaters are integrated into the area PM550 controller systems. However, some clean rooms require, in addition, their own relatively sophisticated PM550 control system to provide closer control than that provided by the general use system. All of these subsystems are coordinated by the central computer which continually monitors system status and energy utilization.

Note the operator terminals at each PM550 station. At any given time, the control programs and controlled elements at any given PM550 station can be changed at the station by adding input/output modules and by changing the program at the station's operator terminal. The programs and control strategies also can be modified from the central control computer. This makes it easy to try different ways to control different parts of the system to see which ones offer the most energy savings. PM550 stations can be added to the system without affecting the operation of the other PM550 stations. Similarly, certain stations can be turned off or removed without affecting the performance of the other stations.

The programmable controller system provides these advantages:

1. The control of the utilization of energy is located at one central point.
2. It provides up-to-date data on energy utilization on which to base current or projected decisions.
3. It is easily changed as equipment or system requirements change.
4. New control strategies can be investigated with changes only in software (programs).

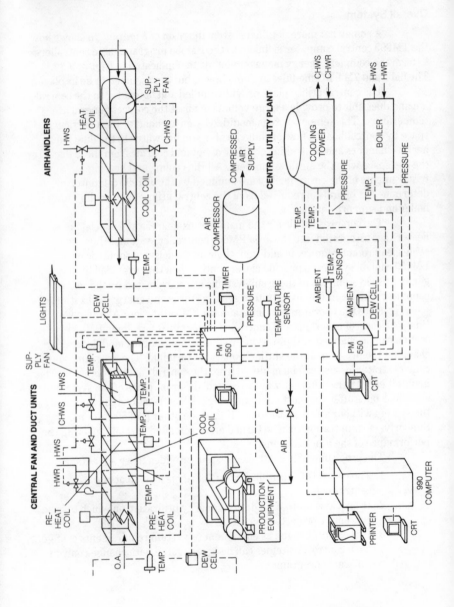

Figure 9-16. *Complete System with Central Computer*

CAN SAVINGS BE EXPECTED FROM THE USE OF PROGRAMMABLE CONTROL SYSTEMS?

The performance of the system described in *Figures 9-12* through *9-16* has been monitored over several years. The results have shown a substantial savings in energy and improvement in system operating convenience over the non-programmable control methods that were used in the past for the same facilities.

Month-By-Month Comparison

Some system parameters are needed to make conclusive comparisons. Two such parameters, shown in *Figure 9-17*, are electrical power consumption and boiler natural gas consumption. They are plotted month-by-month for the system using conventional control techniques (BASE) and for the Programmable Controller (LEVEL 7) system. The average electrical consumption of the BASE system as shown in *Figure 9-17a*, is around 1,400,000 kilowatt-hours (KWH). With the utilization of all the features of the programmable control system, the LEVEL 7 consumption varies from 800,000 to 1,100,000 KWH. The programmable controller system approach produced savings in electrical power consumption for a facility ranging from 24% in the summer months to 42% in the winter months.

The boiler natural gas consumption curve in *Figure 9-17b* shows a peak BASE consumption rate in the winter months of 5,000 million cubic feet (MCF) while the programmable controlled system used only 1,500 MCF. This is a dramatic savings of 3,500 MCF, or 70%, in the boiler energy during the winter. The summer period offers a less dramatic, but significant, savings for the programmable controller system. Even during this low use period, the programmable controller system used only about 500 MCF per month, compared to the 1,200 MCF for the BASE system—a savings of about 58%.

Annual Comparison

Another way of expressing the savings is to plot the annual total energy costs using various system options, as shown in *Figure 9-18a*. For reference, BASE is the same non-programmable conventional system plotted in *Figure 9-17*. The LEVEL 1 option shown in *Figure 9-18a* uses only the ON/OFF PM550 control stations with no central control computer, and all other PM550 subsystems (central utility, air handler, clean room, exhaust fans, and production equipment controllers) inactive. Even with such a small portion of the overall system in operation, there is a significant savings.

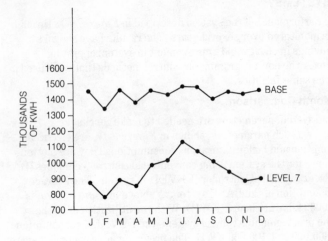

a. Electrical Consumption

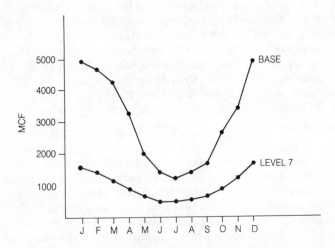

b. Boiler Natural Gas Consumption

BASE – NON-PROGRAMMABLE CONTROL SYSTEM

LEVEL 7 – PROGRAMMABLE CONTROL SYSTEM

Figure 9-17. *Effect of Programmable Control on Monthly Energy Expenditures*

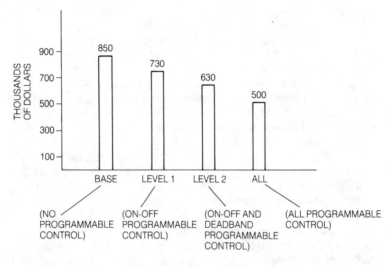

a. Comparison of Annual Costs
Using Different Amounts of Programmable Control

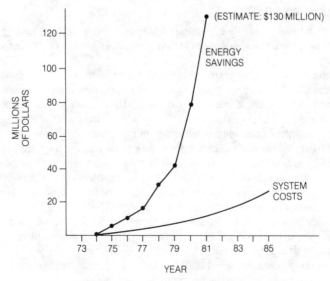

b. Cumulative Savings of Programmable Control versus
Conventional Control Systems

Figure 9-18. *Performance of Programmable Control System*

Annual total energy costs are reduced from $850,000 for the BASE system to $730,000—a 14% savings. If the temperature deadband control subsystems which includes fresh air cooling, and variable air volume, are added to the ON/OFF control subsystem, the total annual energy costs are plotted as LEVEL 2. (Recall that the deadband strategy is to heat air only if the air temperature drops below 70°F and to cool air only if the air temperature goes above 76°F.) Under these conditions, the annual costs are reduced to $630,000 —a 26% savings over the BASE system. When all the PM550 subsystems are included, along with the TM990 central control computer, the result is as shown in the bar for ALL. This indicates an annual total energy cost of about $500,000—a 41% savings in the annual energy bill as compared to the BASE system.

Figure 9-18b presents the impact of the programmable control system in a different manner. If the annual savings of the system with all units active are allowed to accumulate over the years that the system is in operation, the benefits of installing the programmable controller system are seen to be very dramatic and significant. As energy costs increase much faster than system component costs, the savings increase significantly, even after deducting the costs of the programmable controller stations and central computer. The dollar amounts shown in *Figure 9-18b* are for a total plant area of 8 million square feet while the information presented in *Figure 9-18a* deals with a single building of the total plant complex.

WHAT HAVE WE LEARNED?

1. A programmable controller system is one whose behavior is defined by the system program, the sequence of instructions stored in the controller's memory.
2. The components of a programmable controller system are the processor, memory, input devices, output devices, and communications terminals.
3. Programmable controllers have standard hardware modules that make both initial design and later changes easy. The standard hardware is adapted to a particular control situation by the programming.
4. The hardware design of a controller consists of identifying the hardware required; i.e., switches, relays, sensors, actuators, and the appropriate input and output modules as required; then connecting them to the selected programmable controller. An appropriate terminal for programming and communication, and additional memory complete the system.
5. Programming the system consists of developing a ladder diagram from the system component logic and entering this logic into the system memory as a program with a programmer.
6. Programming is accomplished easily by using a language that relates the ladder diagram directly to the program instructions.
7. Significant energy savings are possible when using programmable controller systems to manage the energy utilization for a manufacturing facility.

Quiz for Chapter 9

1. Draw the ladder logic diagrams for the circuits shown below

a.

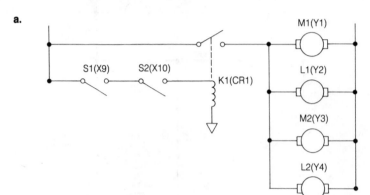

b.

c.

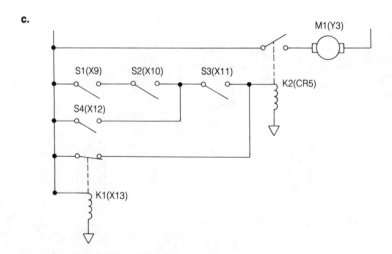

2. Write the TI Model 510 control programs for the following ladder logic diagrams:

a.

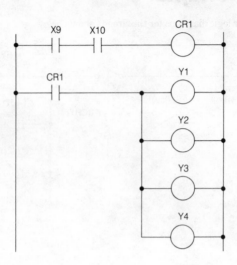

b.

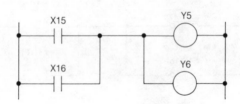

c.

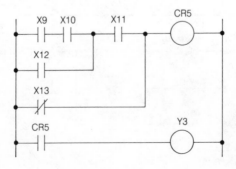

A | Appendix

Appendix

CONVERSION FACTORS—BETWEEN ENGLISH AND METRIC

The conversion factors to convert between English and metric units are given in *Table A-1*. To convert between units, multiply the known value by the factor in the column of the known unit.

EXAMPLE: 200 pounds = 200 × 0.4536 = 90.72 kilograms

Table A-1. *English-Metric Unit Conversion Factors*

Variable	English Units	Metric Units
Length	1 foot = 0.3048 meter	1 meter = 3.281 feet
Mass	1 pound = 0.4536 kilogram 1 slug = 32.17 pounds mass	1 kilogram = 2.205 pounds
Force	1 pound = 0.4536 kilogram 1 pound = 4.448 newtons	1 newton = 0.2248 pound 1 newton = 0.102 kilogram
Pressure	1 atmosphere = 14.7 pounds per square inch	1 atmosphere = 101,300 newtons/meter^2
	1 pound/foot^2 = 47.88 newtons/meter^2	1 newton/meter^2 = 0.2089 pounds/foot^2
Density	1 pound/foot^3 = 16.02 kilograms/meter^3	1 kilogram/meter^3 = 0.06243 pounds/foot^3
Temperature	°F = (9/5 × °C) + 32	°C = 5/9 × (°F − 32)

CONVERSION FACTORS—ENERGY UNITS

To convert energy units of one type energy to another, use *Table A-2*. To find the energy unit in terms of the column unit for a given energy unit in the row, multiply the row quantity by the column factor.

Table A-2. *Energy Unit Conversion Factors*

	Unit	Mechanical Energy		Electrical Energy		Thermal Energy	
		ft-lbs	hp-hr	joules	KWH	Btu	Kcal
Mechanical Energy	ft-lbs	1	5.051×10^{-7}	1.356	3.766×10^{-7}	0.001285	0.0003239
	hp-hr	1,980,000	1	2,685,000	0.7457	2545	641.4
	joules	0.7376	3.725×10^{-7}	1	2.778×10^{-7}	0.0009481	0.0002389
Electrical Energy	KWH	2,655,000	1.341	3,600,000	1	3413	860.1
Thermal Energy	Btu	777.9	0.0003929	1055	0.000293	1	0.252
	Kcal	3087	0.001559	4186	0.001163	3.968	1

CONVERSION FACTORS—POWER UNITS

To convert power units of one type energy to another, use *Table A-3*. To find the energy units in terms of the column unit for a given energy unit in the row, multiply the row quantity by the column factor.

Table A-3. *Power Unit Conversion Factors*

	Unit	Mechanical Power		Electrical Power	Thermal Power	
		Foot-Pounds/Second (ft-lb/sec)	Horsepower (hp)	Kilowatts (KW)	Btu/Hour	Kilocalories/Second (Kcal/sec)
Mechanical Power	ft-lb/sec	1	0.001818	0.001356	4.628	0.0003239
	hp	550	1	0.7457	2545	0.1782
Electrical Power	KW	737.6	1.341	1	3413	0.2389
Thermal Power	Btu/hour	0.2161	0.0003929	0.000293	1	7×10^{-5}
	Kcal/sec	3087	5.613	4.186	14,290	1

Glossary

Air-to-Fuel (A/F): The ratio of the air mass to fuel mass in an internal combustion engine.

Alternating Current (AC): A current that alternates in magnitude and direction, usually periodically. The period of repetition of the alternating pattern is the time between identical points on the waveform.

Amplifier: A device used to increase signal power or amplitude.

Analog: A type of signal whose level varies smoothly and continuously in amplitude or frequency.

Analog-to-Digital (A/D): The conversion of a sampled analog signal to a digital code that represents the voltage level of the analog signal at the instant of sampling.

Anticipator: A resistive heater in a room thermostat that causes the thermostat contacts to open before the room temperature reaches the set temperature.

Armature (See Rotor): The rotating part of a generator or motor that has wound wire coils that connect to an external circuit.

Boiling Water Reactor (BWR): A fission reactor cooled by water which is allowed to boil and produce steam in the reactor vessel.

Capacitor (or Condenser): An electrical component that stores electrical energy and prevents rapid changes of voltage across its terminals.

Chemical Energy: A form of potential energy stored in the atomic and molecular structure of chemical compounds.

Closed-Loop System: A control system in which information from the output is fed back and compared to the input to generate an error signal. This error signal is then used to generate the new output signal.

Commutator: A mechanical-electrical switch on the shaft of a generator or motor to control the direction of current through the armature windings.

Comparator: A device whose output is a digital 0 or 1 depending on whether the input signal is above or below a given reference level.

Conduction: The process that allows heat or electricity to move through a material.

Contactor: A relay designed to switch large amounts of current at power line voltages.

Convection: The process that allows heat to move through air or other gases.

Counter Electromotive Force (CEMF): The voltage produced across the armature windings of a electric motor as a result of generator action. The CEMF opposes the applied voltage which reduces armature current and helps regulate motor speed.

Current: The flow of electrons through a conductive material. The current flow in amperes is proportional to the voltage (in volts) across the material divided by the resistance (in ohms) of the material.

Decoder: A circuit that delivers a pulse to one of 2^n lines as selected by an n-bit binary code.

Digital: Information in discrete or quantized form; not continuous. Binary digital signals have one of two states (0 or 1) defined by voltage or current levels.

Digital-to-Analog (D/A): The conversion of a digital code into its equivalent analog signal level.

Diode: An electronic device that conducts current in only one direction.

Direct Current (DC): A current that flows in only one direction. Its magnitude may change, but its direction does not.

Driver: A circuit that produces a high-power current or voltage output signal from a low-power digital input signal.

Encoder: A circuit that delivers an n-bit binary code that corresponds to the one of 2^n lines that has an input signal on it.

Energy: The capacity for doing work.

Execution: The phase of a computer instruction cycle during which the instruction operation is actually performed.

Fast Breeder Reactor: A nuclear reactor in which the fission reaction not only generates fast neutrons to sustain the reaction, but also breeds more fuel than is consumed.

Fetch: The phase of a computer instruction cycle during which the next instruction to be executed is obtained from system memory.

Field Winding: The winding of a motor or generator that produces the "stationary" magnetic field.

Filter: An electronic device designed to pass signals in a selected frequency range and block signals outside this frequency range.

Fission: An atomic reaction in which one atom splits to form two or more new atoms. Each new atom has a lower number of neutrons in the nucleus than in the original atom.

Flip-Flop: A digital device that is designed to store one binary digit (bit) of information as a 0 or a 1.

Force: An action that tends to cause a mass to move. If the mass is free to move, it will be accelerated by an amount proportional to the force.

Fuel Cell: A device that converts chemical energy to electrical energy by separating atoms into ions and electrons.

Fuel Rod: A small diameter rod composed of fissionable material which provides the fuel for a fission reactor.

Fusion: An atomic reaction in the presence of extremely high temperature and pressure in which one atom is combined with another atom to form a product atom.

Gate: A digital device that performs a logical function such as AND, OR, NOT, and XOR.

Generator (Electrical): A device that converts mechanical energy into electrical energy.

Heat Exchanger: A device in which heat is transferred from one fluid to another while maintaining physical separation of the fluids.

Heat Pump: An efficient heating and cooling machine that uses a refrigeration cycle.

Hexadecimal Numbers: Numbers whose base is 16 instead of 10. The letters A-F represent the decimal numbers 10-15.

Infrared Radiation: The principle radiation that heats the earth. Infrared frequencies are just below those of visible light radiation.

Integrated Circuit (IC): A device in which all of the components of an electronic circuit are fabricated on a single piece of semiconductor material often called a chip. The resultant complete circuit with external connection pins is placed in a plastic or metal package for use as an operational unit.

Integrator: An electronic circuit that performs the mathematical operation of integration. The output signal is proportional to the area under the input signal waveform when the input signal is plotted against time.

Kinetic Energy: The energy stored in a mass in motion moving at a certain velocity.

Ladder Logic Diagram: The diagram that is used to describe the logical interconnection of the electrical wiring of control systems.

Light Radiation: Radiation that is visible to the human eye.

Lumen: A unit used to measure the amount of energy in a beam of light.

Magnetic Field: A field that summarizes the lines of force and energy storage generated by the movement of a charged particle.

Memory: A computer subsystem used to store instructions and data in the form of binary codes.

Moderator: A material used in fission reactors to slow down reaction neutrons.

Motor: A device that converts electrical energy into mechanical energy.

Neutron: An uncharged particle that is part of the nucleus of an atom.

Nuclear Energy: The energy, stored in atomic structures, that results when mass is converted into energy.

Open-Loop System: A control system whose output is a function of only the inputs to the system.

Parallel Data: The transmission or processing of an n-bit binary code n-bits at a time.

Peak Value: The maximum value of a signal in one direction.

Photovoltaic Cell: Also solar cell. A device that converts radiation into electrical energy.

Potential Energy: The energy associated with the relative position of a material mass.

Power: The rate of doing work.

Pressure: The measurement of the amount of force per unit surface area to which the force is applied.

Pressurized Water Reactor (PWR): A fission reactor cooled by water that is kept at such a high pressure that it remains in its liquid state.

Processor: The central control element of a computer. Sometimes called Central Processing Unit or CPU.

Radiation: Energy that is transmitted from one location to another in the form of electromagnetic waves.

Radioactivity: The state of an atom which causes it to undergo atomic changes with the resulting release of atomic particles and electromagnetic radiation.

Random Access Memory (RAM): A type of memory that can be read from or written into, and in which any location can be accessed directly and as fast as any other location.

Reactor: The portion of a nuclear plant that converts nuclear energy to thermal energy.

Read-Only Memory (ROM): A type of memory whose locations can be accessed directly and read, but cannot be written into.

Refrigeration: The process of removing heat from an area by causing the working fluid to evaporate in a coil in a closed system. The resulting vapor is then compressed and condensed to the liquid state, and the cycle repeats.

Register: A device that temporarily stores an n-bit binary code.

Relay: An electromagnetic device with a coil and an isolated set of contacts. The contacts are closed or opened to control a large current flow with only a small current through the control coil.

Resistor: A component whose current is proportional to the voltage applied and to the electrical conductivity of the material from which it is constructed.

Root-Mean-Square (RMS): A means of calculating the value of an ac current or voltage that produces the same amount of power dissipation in a resistor as that same value of dc current or voltage.

Rotor: The rotating part of an electrical motor that has shorted loop conductors that do not connect to an external circuit. Circulating current in the conductors is produced by generator action.

Serial Data: The transmission or processing of an n-bit binary code in sequence one bit at a time.

Silicon Controlled Rectifier (SCR): An electronic device that conducts current when its anode is positive with respect to the cathode and it receives a gate pulse. It doesn't conduct when its anode is negative with respect to its cathode. A TRIAC is two SCRs connected in reverse parallel.

Thermal Energy: The energy associated with raising or lowering the temperature of a material.

Thermistor: A component whose resistance varies significantly and predictably with temperature.

Thermocouple: A junction between two dissimilar materials that produces a voltage that is a function of the temperature of the junction.

Three-Phase Power: AC power that consists of three voltage (and current) signals that have the same peak amplitude, but are displaced 120 electrical degrees with respect to each other.

Three-State Output: An output from an electronic circuit that has three states—active high, active low or high impedance.

Torque: Rotational force that is associated with twisting a shaft.

Transformer: An electrical component that transforms electrical voltage (or current) from one magnitude to another with very little loss of power.

TRIAC: (See SCR)

Turbine: A machine that converts pressure of a fluid to rotational mechanical energy.

Ultraviolet Radiation: Radiation whose frequencies are higher than that of visible radiation.

Voltage: The electrical force or pressure that forces electrons to move through conductive materials.

Work: The product of the force applied to an object times the distance over which the object moves.

Zero-Crossing Detector: A device that outputs a pulse every time its input signal crosses the zero value.

Index

Answers to Quizzes

Chapter 1
1. b
2. d
3. b
4. a
5. d
6. g
7. b
8. c
9. a
10. b
11. d
12. a

Chapter 2
1. a
2. c
3. e
4. b
5. b
6. d
7. b
8. b
9. c
10. c
11. b
12. b

Chapter 3
1. b
2. c
3. b
4. d
5. c
6. d
7. e
8. d
9. d
10. d
11. a
12. b
13. c
14. a
15. f
16. a
17. b
18. b
19. c
20. d

Chapter 4
1. e
2. c
3. f
4. d
5. a
6. c
7. a
8. b
9. d
10. d
11. e

Chapter 5
1. d
2. c
3. c
4. a
5. b
6. a
7. a
8. d
9. a
10. e

Chapter 6
1. c
2. d
3. b
4. b
5. b
6. e
7. b
8. c
9. d
10. a
11. e
12. c
13. a
14. c
15. b
16. d
17. c
18. b
19. e
20. d

Chapter 7
1. c
2. b
3. c
4. d
5. b
6. a
7. d
8. a
9. a
10. d
11. e
12. a
13. d
14. b
15. c
16. c
17. c
18. c
19. d
20. c

Chapter 8
1. b
2. e
3. e
4. d
5. e
6. a
7. c
8. a
9. b
10. c
11. c
12. b
13. c
14. a
15. g
16. g
17. d
18. d
19. a
20. a

Chapter 9
1. The answers for 1a, 1b and 1c are the diagrams given for quiz questions 2a, 2b and 2c, respectively.

2a. STR X9
AND X10
OUT CR1
STR CR1
OUT Y1
OUT Y2
OUT Y3
OUT Y4

2b. STR X15
OR X16
OUT Y5
OUT Y6

2c. STR X9
AND X10
OR X12
AND X11
OR NOT X13
OUT CR5
STR CR5
OUT Y3